MATHEMATICAL CENTRE TRACTS

9

54-32

MATHEMATICAL CENTRE TRACTS

9

UNIVERSAL MORPHISMS

BY

P.C. BAAYEN

MATHEMATISCH CENTRUM AMSTERDAM

1964

MATHEMATICAL CENTRE TRACTS

9

UNIVERSAL MORPHISMS

BY

P.C. BAAYEN

MATHEMATISCH CENTRUM AMSTERDAM

1964

To Leny

CONTENTS

INTRODUCTION AND SUMMARY

A well-known theorem of A. TYCHONOV asserts that the cube (topological product of segments) P_κ of weight κ (where κ is any transfinite cardinal number) is a universal completely regular space of weight κ. More recently it has been proved that there even exists a universal system F of κ continuous self-maps in P_κ: if X is any completely regular space of weight at most κ, and if S is any semigroup of at most κ continuous self-maps of X, then the action of S is topologically equivalent to the action of F, restricted to a suitable F-invariant subspace of P_κ (cf. [47,49]).

The fundamental idea on which the proof of the latter result is based is surprisingly simple. It is sketched in the notes of chapter 2; may it suffice here to say that it amounts essentially to considering the orbits under S of points $x \in X$ as points of a new space.

This basic idea turned out to be of much value in other situations too. Thus J. DE GROOT and the author used it to solve (in the affirmative) a problem raised by R.D. ANDERSON concerning the existence of universal homeomorphisms in the discontinuum of Cantor (P.C. BAAYEN [6]). By exactly the same device G.-C. ROTA [90,91] proved the existence of universal contraction operators in Hilbert spaces.

These observations motivated an investigation of the basic construction in a general setting; the theory of categories turned out to be suitable for this purpose.

Let us say that a morphism $\alpha : A \to A$ of a category K is equivalent to a restriction of a morphism $\beta : B \to B$ in K if there exists a monomorphism $\mu : A \to B$ such that $\mu\beta = \alpha\mu$. We will call a morphism $\beta : B \to B$ in K <u>universal</u> in K, if every (endo-) morphism $\alpha : A \to A$ in K is equivalent to a restriction of β. Then, as turns out, the basic construction alluded to above can be simulated in abstract categories in order to obtain a rather general sufficient condition for the existence of universal morphisms.

Before developing this theory we collect in chapter 1 several concepts and results from the extant literature which we need in the sequel, supplementing them where necessary. Thus in sections 1.1 and 1.2 the basic concepts from the theory of categories are introduced, a list of concrete categories is given (to be used for concrete applications of the general results, and also furnishing material for some counter-examples), and the monomorphisms and epimorphisms in these categories are determined as far as possible.

If $\beta : B \to B$ is a universal morphism in a category K, then B necessarily is a universal object, in the sense that for an arbitrary object A of K there exists a monomorphism $\mu : A \to B$. It is therefore indispensable to know about the existence of universal objects preliminary to an exploration of universal morphisms. Fortunately many results on universal objects are available in the literature; several of them are brought together in section 1.4. As a very important and powerful theorem in this direction is the one of B. JÓNSSON [60,61] on universal relational systems, we have inserted a section introducing the relevant terminology (section 1.3).

In section 1.5 the structure of order-preserving maps in linearly ordered sets is analysed as far as is necessary for a proof (in the next chapter) of the existence of universal morphisms in categories of linearly ordered spaces. These categories are exceptional (we will return to this fact); except in section 2.7, the results of section 1.5 will nowhere be used.

The final section of chapter 1, and more generally the final section of each chapter, contains notes and additions to the material presented in the chapter concerned; in particular, references to the extant literature and sources of theorems quoted are liberally and extensively presented.

In chapter 2 the fundamental construction alluded to above is developed and studied in the setting of category theory. First universal morphisms are defined, and with them universal bimorphisms and universal systems of morphisms. In addition, the dual concepts are introduced (section 2.1).

In the next two sections special morphisms are considered; these morphisms are analogous to those self-maps of cartesian products X^A which only change the arrangement of the coordinates of points $(x_\alpha)_{\alpha \in A} \in X^A$. The results of these sections are used in section 2.4 to obtain a simple sufficient condition on a category K in order that it contains universal morphisms:

THEOREM 1. If K contains a universal object u, and if moreover a direct join of denumerably many copies of u exists in K, then K contains universal morphisms.

(We derive a more general form, dealing with universal systems of morphisms; the considerations are also extended to morphisms which are only universal with respect to a subcategory K_o of K. Dual results are also formulated).

There exist many applications of the existence theorems of section 2.4. Several are treated in section 2.5. By way of example we mention:

THEOREM 2. Let κ be a transfinite cardinal number. There exists an automorphism (endomorphism) $\Phi : A \to A$ of a group (abelian group, boolean algebra, distributive lattice) A which is universal for all automorphisms (endomorphisms) $\varphi : B \to B$ of an arbitrary group (abelian group, boolean algebra, distributive lattice) B such that card(B) $\leqq \kappa$. If the Generalized Continuum Hypothesis holds, and if furthermore $\kappa^{\aleph_0} = \kappa$, it can be obtained in addition that card(A) $= \kappa$.

THEOREM 3. There exists a continuous automorphism (endomorphism) Φ of the infinite torus which is universal for all continuous automorphisms (endomorphisms) of arbitrary compact metrizable abelian groups.

Similar results are obtained concerning the existence of universal continuous self-maps or autohomeomorphisms of metrizable spaces or compact zero-dimensional Hausdorff spaces of limited weight, and concerning universal order-preserving maps in partially ordered spaces. All these results are extended to universal <u>systems</u> of morphisms.

Some applications of a dual nature are the following:

THEOREM 4. Let κ be a transfinite cardinal number. There exists a group (abelian group, semigroup with unit, boolean algebra, distributive lattice) A, with card(A) = κ, and an automorphism (endomorphism) $\Phi : A \to A$, with the following property. If B is any group (abelian group, semigroup with unit, boolean algebra, distributive lattice) with card(B) $\leqq \kappa$, and if $\varphi : B \to B$ is any automorphism (endomorphism) of B, then φ can be raised to Φ.

THEOREM 5. There exists a continuous automorphism (endomorphism) Φ of a compact solenoidal group G to which every continuous automorphism (endomorphism) φ of an arbitrary compact solenoidal group H can be continuously raised.

Moreover, examples are given of categories K which admit universal objects but contain no universal morphism. It is also shown that the sufficient condition of theorem 1 is not necessary: in section 2.7 we prove that no direct joins exist in the category of all order-preserving maps between linearly ordered sets (except in some trivial cases), and that nevertheless order-preserving self-maps exist which are universal for all such self-maps of linearly ordered sets S with card(S) $\leqq \kappa$ (κ an arbitrary transfinite cardinal number).

In the third chapter attention is given to categories of topological spaces. In these categories the results of chapter 2 can be sharpened in the following sense: both in definitions and assertions we may replace the terms "monomorphism" and "epimorphism" by "topological mapping into" and "continuous mapping onto", respectively. These concepts are more natural, in a topological context. Similarly topological products (sums) are more interesting, from a topological point of view, than direct (free)joins. Therefore we call a category of topological spaces <u>neat</u> if every direct join is topologically equivalent to a topological product with its natural projections; <u>co-neatness</u> is defined analogously, considering free joins and topological sums. In section 3.2 we examine several categories on neatness and co-neatness. For neat categories a satisfying "topologization" of theorem 1 can be obtained (section 3.3) and analogously (but not dually) the assertion dual to theorem 1 is "topologized" for co-neat categories.

Several applications are presented in section 3.4. Among these are new proofs of some of the results on S-compactifications in J. DE GROOT and R.H. MCDOWELL [51] and of a result on raising to the Cantor set of continuous self-maps of R.D. ANDERSON [4] ;these new proofs also lead to some generalizations. Universal uniformly continuous maps in uniform spaces and universal isometries and contractions in metric spaces are also considered. In section 3.5, finally, we give special attention to the theorem on universal continuous self-maps in completely regular spaces, mentioned in the opening lines of this introduction, and especially to its interpretation as a result on linearization of mappings.

The main result of chapter 4 (theorem 4.3.1) is a generalization of a theorem of J. DE GROOT [49] , asserting that the action of a compact group of autohomeomorphisms of a metrizable space is equivalent to the action of a group G of unitary operators in a Hilbert space H, restricted to a suitable G-invariant subset of H. We show that a locally compact transformation group G acting on a metrizable space M can be linearized by a group of bounded linear operations in some Hilbert space whenever G belongs to a certain class CW. This class CW, introduced in section 4.2, not only comprises all compact groups, but also all countable discrete groups and the additive group of real numbers. Moreover, every subgroup and every continuous homomorphic image of a group in CW is again a CW-group; topological direct products of finitely many CW-groups are once more CW-groups; and each locally compact group G, which contains a compact normal subgroup G_o such that G/G_o is discrete and countable, belongs to CW. It follows that CW contains all locally compact abelian groups which are either separable or compactly generated; of course there also exist many non-abelian CW-groups.

In section 4.4 the (apparently rather meagre) possibilities of extending these results to topological transformation semigroups are discussed. It is shown in section 4.5 how the proof of theorem 4.3.1 implies some results on universal linearizations. Section 4.6 presents additional information for the special case of mappings of finite order and for finite transformation semigroups.

(The results of these first six sections of chapter 4 will also be published separately: P.C. BAAYEN and J. DE GROOT [10]).

Section 4.7 is devoted to universal bounded linear operators of certain types in Hilbert spaces. G.-C. ROTA [90,91] proved that the infinite unilateral (reverse) shift is universal for all operators T of spectral radius less than one. We show that there exists a bounded linear operator which is universal for all T such that all iterates T^n are uniformly bounded in norm. Similar results are obtained for uniformly bounded semigroups of linear operators.

I wish to express my gratitude to J. de Groot, to whom I am deeply indebted. This tract would never have been written but for his continuous interest and encouragement. I am very grateful to G.J. Helmberg, who eliminated a number of errors and suggested several important improvements. I am indebted to R.D. Anderson, Z. Hedrlín, M.A. Maurice and Mrs A.B. Paalman-de Miranda for many stimulating discussions. To Z. Hedrlín I owe moreover the Russian summary at the end of this treatise. Finally I take the opportunity to thank Miss L.J. Noordstar and her staff and D. Zwarst for their typing and printing of the manuscript.

CONVENTIONS AND NOTATIONS

Our considerations are based on a set theory of the J. VON NEUMANN - P. BERNAYS - K. GÖDEL type. Thus every entity is a class; a class is a set if and only if there exists another class of which it is a member.

The Axiom of Choice is used without qualms, and without special mentioning. We postulate it in a class form: "If S is a class of non-empty sets, there is a function Φ such that for each $x \in S$, $(x)\Phi \in x$".

The Generalized Continuum Hypothesis is also used without inhibitions; however, whenever the proof of an assertion relies on an application of this hypothesis, the number indicating this assertion is preceded by an asterisk; e.g. proposition $^*1.4.5$, theorem $^*2.5.8$, etc.

The class of all cardinal numbers is denoted by CARD, the class of all ordinal numbers by ORD; we consider 0 to be an ordinal number. Because of the fact that we accept the Axiom of Choice, every transfinite cardinal number can be represented as an $\aleph_\theta$, $\theta \in$ ORD. The cardinality (power) of a set A is denoted by card(A). A set A is called denumerable if card(A) $= \aleph_0$, and countable if card(A) $\leq \aleph_0$.

If f is a function, Df denotes the domain of f. The class Df need not be a set.

In matters of category theory we use the notation of A.G. KUROSH, A. Kh. LIVSHITS and E.G. SHUL'GEIFER [73]; in particular, if $\alpha: a \to b$ and $\beta: b \to c$, their product will be denoted by $\alpha\beta : a \to c$. Correspondingly the arguments of a function are written before the function symbol, and the composition $f \circ g$ of two maps f and g is the map $x \to ((x)f)g$. Of course it was not possible to adhere to this rule consistently; notable aberrations are notations like H(a,b), S(a,A), $\aleph_\theta$, card(A); there are many others.

The symbol $\prod$ will only be used to designate direct joins in categories, like it is used in [73]. The cartesian product of a family of sets $(A_t)_{t \in T}$ will be denoted by $\mathbb{P}_{t \in T} A_t$.

If f is a function and A is a class, then (A)f and Af stand for $\{af : a \in A \cap Df\}$, while Af^{-1} and $(A)f^{-1}$ stand for $\{a \in Df : af \in A\}$. We use xf^{-1} as an abbreviation for $\{x\}f^{-1}$.

If f is a 1-1 map, the inverse of f is denoted by f^{-1}. This has as a consequence that our notation is inconsistent: if f is a 1-1 map and if $x \in (Df)f$, then xf^{-1} can stand both for the uniquely determined y such that yf = x and for the set $\{y\}$; we trust, however, that in all instances it is clear from the context what is meant.

The set of all non-negative integers is denoted by N; the set of all integers by I; the set of all rational numbers by Q; the set of all real numbers by R.

If A is a set, i_A denotes the identity map on A; i.e. $i_A = \{(a,a) : a \in A\}$. If f is a map, then $f^o = i_{Df}$, $f^{n+1} = f \circ f^n$ $(n \in N)$. If moreover f is 1-1, then $f^{-n} = (f^n)^{-1}$, for $n \in N$.

If A and B are sets, A^B denotes the set of all maps of B into A. If $f \in A^B$ and $\beta \in B$, it occurs frequently that we write f_β instead of $(\beta)f$; then in the same context we write $(f_\beta)_{\beta \in B}$ for f. No distinction is made between the set A^B and the cartesian product $\prod_{\beta \in B} A_\beta$, with $A_\beta = A$ for each $\beta \in B$.

All semigroups considered are supposed to be semigroups with unit, whether this is expressly mentioned in the context or not. A homomorphism of a semigroup S into a semigroup S_2 is always supposed to map the unit of S_1 onto the unit of S_2.

If A is a set, A^A becomes a semigroup if we take composition of functions as its law of composition; if we talk about "the semigroup A^A", we always mean this semigroup. If F is a subsemigroup of A^A, then i_A is supposed to be contained in F (it then follows that i_A is the unit of F).

The (algebraic) weight of an algebraic system A is the least cardinal number of a subset of A generating A.

Every topological space considered is supposed to be Hausdorff, with the exception of one instance in section 1.6 (theorem 1.6.4). The (topological) weight of a topological space X is the minimal cardinal number of an open base for X. If we talk about the weight of of a topological group or a topological linear space we always have in mind the topological weight. By the dimension of a topological space we always mean the small inductive dimension of the space.

We use $\Longrightarrow$ as implication symbol; $\wedge$ and $\vee$ are sparsely used for the logical connectives "and" and "or", respectively, while $\exists$ and $\forall$ occur occasionally as symbols for the existential and universal quantifiers.

1. PRELIMINARIES

1.1. Concepts from the theory of categories

In this section some definitions and results are collected from the theory of categories. For a more extensive exposition of this theory, and for proofs, we refer to the literature. See also the notes to this chapter (section 1.6).

1.1.1. DEFINITION. A category K is a class of elements, called the morphisms of K, in which a partial product is defined, satisfying the conditions below (if the product of $\alpha \in K$ and $\beta \in K$ is defined, we will denote it by $\alpha.\beta$ or $\alpha\beta$):

(i) The triple product $\alpha_1(\alpha_2\alpha_3)$ is defined if and only if $(\alpha_1\alpha_2)\alpha_3$ is defined. When either is defined the associative law

(1) $$\alpha_1(\alpha_2\alpha_3) = (\alpha_1\alpha_2)\alpha_3$$

holds. This triple product will be written as $\alpha_1\alpha_2\alpha_3$.

(ii) The triple product $\alpha_1\alpha_2\alpha_3$ is defined whenever both products $\alpha_1\alpha_2$ and $\alpha_2\alpha_3$ are defined.

(iii) For each $\alpha \in K$ there exist identities $\varepsilon_1, \varepsilon_2 \in K$ such that $\varepsilon_1\alpha$ and $\alpha\varepsilon_2$ are defined (an identity in K is a morphism ε with the property that $\varepsilon\xi = \xi$ whenever $\varepsilon\xi$ is defined and $\xi\varepsilon = \xi$ whenever $\xi\varepsilon$ is defined).

(iv) If ε_1 and ε_2 are identities of K, the class H of all $\alpha \in K$ for which $\varepsilon_1\alpha$ and $\alpha\varepsilon_2$ are both defined is a (possibly empty) set.

1.1.2. PROPOSITION. For each $\alpha \in K$ the identities ε_1 and ε_2 such that $\varepsilon_1\alpha$ and $\alpha\varepsilon_2$ are defined are uniquely determined. We will call them the left and the right identity of α, respectively; in symbols: $\varepsilon_1 = \varepsilon^\alpha$, $\varepsilon_2 = {}^\alpha\varepsilon$. A product $\alpha\beta$ is defined if and only if ${}^\alpha\varepsilon = \varepsilon^\beta$.

1.1.3. DEFINITION. Let K_1 and K_2 be categories, and let Φ be a map of K_1 into K_2. The map Φ is called a covariant functor if it satisfies the following conditions:

(i) if $\alpha_1\alpha_2$ is defined in K_1, then $(\alpha_1\Phi).(\alpha_2\Phi)$ is defined in K_2, and $(\alpha_1\Phi).(\alpha_2\Phi) = (\alpha_1.\alpha_2)\Phi$;

(ii) if ε is an identity morphism in K_1, then $\varepsilon\Phi$ is an identity morphism in K_2.

The map Φ is called a <u>contravariant functor</u> if it satisfies condition (ii), and also

(i^*) if $\alpha_1\alpha_2$ is defined in K_1, then $(\alpha_2\Phi).(\alpha_1\Phi)$ is defined in K_2, and $(\alpha_2\Phi).(\alpha_1\Phi) = (\alpha_1\alpha_2)\Phi$.

The map Φ is called an <u>isomorphism</u> of K_1 onto K_2 if it is a 1-1 covariant functor of K_1 onto K_2 satisfying the additional condition:

(iii) if $(\alpha_1\Phi).(\alpha_2\Phi)$ is defined in K_2, then $\alpha_1\alpha_2$ is defined in K_1.

The map Φ is called an <u>anti-isomorphism</u> of K_1 onto K_2 if it is a 1-1 contravariant functor of K_1 onto K_2 satisfying the additional condition

(iii^*) if $(\alpha_2\Phi).(\alpha_1\Phi)$ is defined in K_2, then $\alpha_1\alpha_2$ is defined in K_1.

1.1.4. DEFINITIONS. A subcategory K_o of a category K is a subclass of K which is a category under the partial product in K. We will consider only such subcategories K_o of K that satisfy the additional condition: whenever $\alpha \in K_o$, the left and right identities ε^α and ${}^\alpha\varepsilon$ of α in K both also belong to K_o.

A subcategory K_o of K is called <u>full</u> if $\alpha \in K_o$ whenever both $\varepsilon^\alpha \in K_o$ and ${}^\alpha\varepsilon \in K_o$.

If K is a category, the <u>dual</u> category K^* is the category that shares with K the class of morphisms, whereas the composition law in K^* is inverse to the composition law in K: if we write, momentarily, $\alpha_1 * \alpha_2$ for the product of α_1 and α_2 in K^*, then $\alpha_1 * \alpha_2$ is defined in K^* and is equal to α_3, if and only if $\alpha_2.\alpha_1$ is defined in K and is equal to α_3.

In other words, the composition law in K^* is chosen in such a way that the identity map $K \to K^*$ becomes an anti-isomorphism.

A standard category is the so-called category of all sets, K(S) in our notation (cf. section 1.2). The morphisms of K(S) are all ordered pairs (f,B), where B is a set and f is a map of a set A into B (thus morphisms of K(S) are pairs of set, f being a subset of $A \times B$. Obviously the set A is completely determined by f, $A=D(f)$; it is as obvious that this is not the case with B, as it is allowed that f is not onto).

If $\alpha_1 \in K(S)$ and $\alpha_2 \in K(S)$, say $\alpha_1 = (f_1, B_1)$ and $\alpha_2 = (f_2, B_2)$, then $\alpha_1 . \alpha_2$ is defined in K(S) if and only if $B_1 = D(f_2)$; in that case we put

(2) $$\alpha_1 . \alpha_2 = (f_1 \circ f_2, B_2).$$

(Thus if B_1 is properly contained in $D(f_2)$, $\alpha_1 . \alpha_2$ is not defined although $f_1 \circ f_2$ is defined. One can easily show that the class of all maps of one set into another, with ordinary composition of maps as product law, is not a category.)

1.1.5. DEFINITION. A category K is concrete if there exists an isomorphism of K onto a subcategory of K(S).

If $K = K(S)$, there is a natural 1-1 correlation between the class of all identities of K and the class of all sets: if ε is an identity of K(S), say $\varepsilon = (f,X)$, then $f = i_X$; conversely, if X is an arbitrary set, the morphism (i_X, X) is an identity of K(S). The set X is called the object correlated with (i_X, X).

For many other categories K there exists a natural 1-1 correlation between the class of all identities of K and a class $\mathcal{O}$ of entities, which then also are called objects. (A class of objects can always be selected, for arbitrary K: just take for $\mathcal{O}$ the very class of all identities of K). If $a \in \mathcal{O}$, the identity of K correlated with a is then denoted by ε_a. If $a \in \mathcal{O}$ and $b \in \mathcal{O}$, the set of all $\alpha \in K$ for which $\varepsilon_a = \varepsilon^{\alpha}$ and $\varepsilon_b = {}^{\alpha}\varepsilon$ is denoted by $H(a,b)$; we write $\alpha \colon a \to b$ synonymously with $\alpha \in H(a,b)$, and we call a and b the first and second object of α, respectively, or also the source and the sink of α. If it is necessary to indicate the category K in which $H(a,b)$ is formed, we write $H_K(a,b)$.

1.1.6. DEFINITION. Let K be a category. A morphism μ of K is called a <u>monomorphism</u>, if, for any α_1, α_2 such that $\alpha_1\mu$, $\alpha_2\mu$ are defined, $\alpha_1\mu = \alpha_2\mu$ implies $\alpha_1 = \alpha_2$. A morphism ν of K is called an <u>epimorphism</u> if, for any $\alpha_1, \alpha_2 \in K$ such that $\nu\alpha_1$, $\nu\alpha_2$ are defined, $\nu\alpha_1 = \nu\alpha_2$ implies $\alpha_1 = \alpha_2$. A <u>bimorphism</u> is a morphism that is both a monomorphism and an epimorphism. A morphism α of K is called <u>invertible</u> if there exists a $\beta \in K$ such that both $\alpha\beta = \varepsilon^{\alpha}$ and $\beta\alpha = {}^{\alpha}\varepsilon$. If α is invertible the morphism β such that $\alpha\beta = \varepsilon^{\alpha}$, $\beta\alpha = {}^{\alpha}\varepsilon$ is uniquely determined; it is called the <u>inverse</u> of α and will be denoted by α^{-1}.

1.1.7. PROPOSITION. Every identity is invertible; every invertible morphism is a bimorphism. If μ_1 and μ_2 are monomorphisms, and if $\mu_1\mu_2$ is defined, then $\mu_1\mu_2$ is a monomorphism; if ν_1 and ν_2 are epimorphisms, so is $\nu_1\nu_2$, if this product is defined. If $\mu_1\mu_2$ is a monomorphism, so is μ_1; if $\nu_1\nu_2$ is an epimorphism, so is ν_2.

1.1.8. DEFINITION. Let K be a category, T a non-void set, and let ε_t be an identity of K for each $t \in T$.

A <u>direct join</u> of the family $(\varepsilon_t)_{t \in T}$ is a family of morphisms $(\pi_t)_{t \in T}$ in K with the following properties:

(i) there exists an identity ε in K such that

$$\varepsilon^{\pi_t} = \varepsilon; \quad {}^{\pi_t}\varepsilon = \varepsilon_t, \tag{3}$$

for each $t \in T$;

(ii) for every family of morphisms $(\alpha_t)_{t \in T}$ in K such that

$$\varepsilon^{\alpha_t} = \eta; \quad {}^{\alpha_t}\varepsilon = \varepsilon_t, \tag{4}$$

for all $t \in T$ (η denoting a suitable identity in K) there exists a uniquely determined $\alpha \in K$, such that $\varepsilon^{\alpha} = \eta$, ${}^{\alpha}\varepsilon = \varepsilon$, and

$$\alpha\pi_t = \alpha_t \tag{5}$$

for all $t \in T$.

Suppose objects are correlated with the identities of K; say a_t is correlated to ε_t, for each $t \in T$, and let d be correlated to ε and b to η. Then, "par abus de language", we say that d is the <u>direct join</u> of the family of objects $(a_t)_{t \in T}$ <u>by means of the projecting morphisms</u> $\pi_t : d \to a_t$, if $(\pi_t)_{t \in T}$ is a direct join of $(\varepsilon_t)_{t \in T}$. In symbols: $d = \prod_{t \in T} a_t(\pi_t)$.

(6)

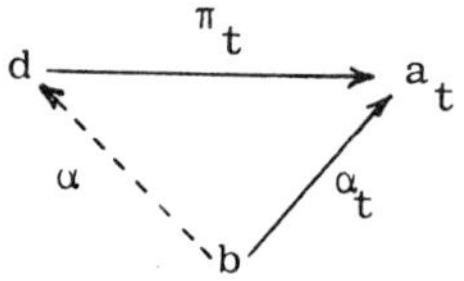

REMARK. It should be kept in mind that the important part in a direct join presentation $d = \prod_{t \in T} a_t \; (\pi_t)$, is the family of morphisms $(\pi_t)_{t \in T}$. This family determines d (or the corresponding identity morphism ε) completely; the converse does not hold.

The concept, dual to the concept of direct join, is called free join:

1.1.9. DEFINITION. Let K be a category, T a non-void set, and let ε_t be an identity of K for each $t \in T$. The family $(\pi_t)_{t \in T}$ in K is a <u>free join</u> of the family $(\varepsilon_t)_{t \in T}$ if in the dual category K^* it is a direct join of $(\varepsilon_t)_{t \in T}$.

If objects are correlated to the identities of K, we will say that the object d is a free join of the family of objects $(a_t)_{t \in T}$ <u>by means of the injecting morphisms</u> $(\pi_t)_{t \in T}$, in symbols

(7)
$$d = \mathop{\ast}_{t \in T} a_t \; (\pi_t),$$

whenever $(\pi_t)_{t \in T}$ is a free join of $(\varepsilon_{a_t})_{t \in T}$.

(8)

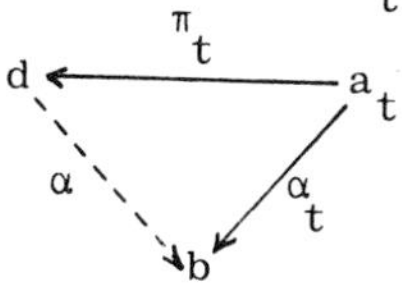

If this is the case, then whenever a family $(\alpha_t)_{t \in T}$, $\alpha_t : a_t \to b$, in K is given there exists a uniquely determined $\alpha : a \to b$ in K such that $\alpha_t = \pi_t \alpha$, for all $t \in T$.

1.1.10. DEFINITION. A direct join (free join) $(\pi_t)_{t \in T}$ of a family $(\varepsilon_t)_{t \in T}$ of identities in a category K is called <u>strong</u> if $\pi_s \neq \pi_t$ for distinct $s, t \in T$.

The following notational convention will turn out to be useful:

1.1.11. DEFINITION. Let K be a category and T a non-void set. If ε is an identity of K, we will write $S(\varepsilon, T)$ for the family $(\varepsilon_t)_{t \in T}$ with $\varepsilon_t = \varepsilon$ for all $t \in T$. The class of all direct joins in K of $S(\varepsilon, T)$ will be denoted by $\Delta(\varepsilon, T)$; of course this class may well be empty.

If objects are correlated to the identities of K, we will write $S(a,T)$ instead of $S(\varepsilon_a, T)$ and $\Delta(a,T)$ instead of $\Delta(\varepsilon_a, T)$. If $(\pi_t)_{t \in T} \in \Delta(a,T)$, and if d is the object such that $\varepsilon_d = \varepsilon^{\pi_t}$, for all $t \in T$, we write

(9) $$d = \prod S(a,T) \quad (\pi_t).$$

1.1.12. PROPOSITION. Let $d = \prod_{t \in T} a_t \quad (\pi_t)$, and let the morphisms $\beta_1 : b \to d$ and $\beta_2 : b \to d$ be such that $\beta_1 \pi_t = \beta_2 \pi_t$, for all $t \in T$. Then $\beta_1 = \beta_2$.

1.1.13. PROPOSITION. Let $d = \prod_{t \in T} a_t \quad (\pi_t)$ and $e = \prod_{t \in T} b_t \quad (\rho_t)$, and let $\alpha_t : a_t \to b_t$, for every $t \in T$. There exists a uniquely determined morphism $\alpha : d \to e$ in K such that $\pi_t \alpha_t = \alpha \rho_t$, for all $t \in T$. If all α_t are monomorphisms, then α is also a monomorphism.

(10) $$\begin{array}{ccc} d & \xrightarrow{\pi_t} & a_t \\ {\scriptstyle\alpha}\downarrow & & \downarrow{\scriptstyle\alpha_t} \\ e & \xrightarrow{\rho_t} & b_t \end{array}$$

CONVENTION: <u>From now on we will always assume objects to be correlated to the identities of the categories considered.</u>

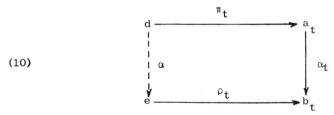

1.2. Description of some concrete categories

A number of concrete categories that will be referred to in the sequel are collected and described in this section. We discuss in particular the monomorphisms and epimorphisms in each of these categories.

1.2.1. List of categories

K(S) - category of all mappings of one set into another.

K(LO) - category of all order-preserving maps of one linearly ordered set into another one.

K(PO) - category of all order-preserving maps of one partially ordered set into another.

K(La) - category of all lattice-homomorphisms of one lattice into another lattice.

K(DLa) - the full subcategory of K(La) obtained by admitting as objects only distributive lattices.

K(BA) - category of all boolean homomorphisms of one boolean algebra into another one.

K(SGU) - category of all homomorphisms of one semigroup with unit S_1 into another semigroup with unit S_2, that send the unit of S_1 into the unit of S_2.

K(G) - the full subcategory of K(SGU) obtained by admitting only groups as objects.

K(AG) - the full subcategory of K(SGU) obtained by admitting only abelian groups as objects.

K(M) - category of all continuous maps of one metrizable space into another one.

K(ZM) - category of all continuous maps of one zero-dimensional metrizable space into another.

K(CZ) - category of all continuous maps of one compact zero-dimensional space into another such a space.

K(CR) - category of all continuous maps of one completely regular Hausdorff space into another.

K(H) - category of all bounded linear operators of one Hilbert space into another.

K(CMAG) - category of all continuous homomorphisms of a compact metrizable abelian group into another compact metrizable abelian group.

K(CMoG) - category of all continuous homomorphisms of one compact monothetic group into another.

(D. VAN DANTZIG [20] introduced the concept of a monothetic group. According to his definition, a topological group is called monothetic if it contains a dense infinite cyclic subgroup. Following current usage, we slightly modify his definition, and call a topological group monothetic if and only if it contains a dense cyclic subgroup. In a later publication [25], D. VAN DANTZIG himself used "monothetic" in this sense.)

1.2.2. DEFINITION. If K is a concrete category, and θ an ordinal number, then $K(\theta)$ denotes the full subcategory of K obtained by admitting as objects only those objects of K which have cardinality $\leq \aleph_\theta$.

Instead of $K(S)(\theta)$ we write $K(S,\theta)$; a similar notation is used for the other categories mentioned in 1.2.1.

For topological spaces the weight of the space turns out to be a more interesting cardinal number then its power. Therefore we introduce:

1.2.3. Let $\theta \in$ ORD, and let K be one of the categories K(M), K(ZM), K(CZ), K(CR), K(H). Then K^θ denotes the full subcategory of K obtained by admitting as objects only those spaces that have a (topological) weight $\leq \aleph_\theta$.

It is important to know which morphisms μ of a given category K are monomorphisms, and which morphisms ν are epimorphisms.

1.2.4. PROPOSITION. In all categories of the list 1.2.1, and in their subcategories obtained as indicated in 1.2.2 and 1.2.3, the monomorphisms are exactly the morphisms that are 1-1 maps.

PROOF. Clearly 1-1 maps are always monomorphisms. Assume the morphism $\mu : a \to b$ is not 1-1 : let $\xi_1\mu = \xi_2\mu$, where $\xi_1, \xi_2 \in a$, $\xi_1 \neq \xi_2$.

If K is one of the categories K(S), K(LO), K(PO), K(M), K(ZM), K(CZ), K(CR), or one of their subcategories $K(S,\theta)$, $K(LO,\theta)$, $K(PO,\theta)$, $K^{\theta}(ZM)$, $K^{\theta}(CZ)$, $K^{\theta}(CR)$ $(\theta \in ORD)$, there exist in K morphisms ϕ_1, ϕ_2, both mapping a into a, such that $a\phi_i = \{\xi_i\}$ $(i=1,2)$. Then $\phi_1 \neq \phi_2$ but $\phi_1\mu = \phi_2\mu$; hence μ is not a monomorphism.

If K has algebraic systems for objects, i.e. if it is one of the following categories: K(La), K(DLa), K(BA), K(SGU), K(G), K(AG); $K(La,\theta), \ldots, K(AG,\theta)$ $(\theta \in ORD)$, we reason as follows. Let c be an object of K that is a free algebraic system of the kind considered. There exist morphisms $\phi_i : c \to a$ in K such that ϕ_i sends all free generators of c into ξ_i $(i=1,2)$. Then again $\phi_1 \neq \phi_2$, $\phi_1\mu = \phi_2\mu$, showing that μ is not a monomorphism.

A similar reasoning can be used if K is one of the categories K(H), $K^{\theta}(H)$ $(\theta \in ORD)$.

If K = K(CMAG) we proceed in the following manner. Let a_o be the kernel of the continuous homomorphism μ; then a_o is an object of K. Let ϕ_1 be the canonical embedding $a_o \to a$, and let ϕ_2 map a_o onto the neutral element of a. Then $\phi_1 \neq \phi_2$ whereas $\phi_1\mu = \phi_2\mu$.

Finally let K = K(CMoG). Let ξ_o be an element of the kernel of μ, different from the neutral element of a, and let a_o be the closed subgroup of a generated by ξ_o. Let T be the circle group, t a generator of a dense cyclic subgroup of T, and c the closed subgroup of the direct product of T and a_o generated by the element (t, ξ_o). Then c is a compact monothetic group. Let ϕ_1 be the restriction to c of the canonical homomorphism $T \times a_o \to a_o$, considered as a map $c \to a$; let $\phi_2 : c \to a$ map c into the neutral element of a. Then $\phi_1 \neq \phi_2$ although $\phi_1\mu = \phi_2\mu$; hence μ is not a monomorphism.

In categories of topological spaces the interesting 1-1 maps are the topological mappings into. These maps are of course monomorphisms; but proposition 1.2.4 shows that in general there are other monomorphisms. However:

1.2.5. PROPOSITION. If K is one of the categories K(CMAG), K(CMoG), K(CZ), K(H); K^{θ}(CZ), K^{θ}(H) ($\theta \in$ ORD), the monomorphisms of K are just the topological embedding maps.

PROOF. If K is one of the categories K(H) or K^{θ}(H), the assertion is a consequence of 1.2.4 and S. BANACH's Inverse Operator Theorem ([12] Ch.III, §3 theorem 5). In all other cases the assertion follows because all objects of K are compact spaces.

We start the discussion of epimorphisms in the categories of 1.2.1 by considering the cases where epimorphisms need not be mappings onto.

1.2.6. PROPOSITION. Let K be one of the categories K(M), K(ZM), K(CR); K^{θ}(M), K^{θ}(ZM), K^{θ}(CR) ($\theta \in$ ORD). Then the epimorphisms of K are exactly those continuous maps that have a dense image.

PROOF. Clearly every continuous map with a dense image is an epimorphism. Now let $\nu : a \to b$ be a morphism of K such that $a\nu$ is not dense in b. Take $\eta \in b \setminus \overline{a\nu}$, and let ϕ_1, ϕ_2 be continuous maps of b into the unit segment $[0,1]$ such that $(\overline{a\nu})\phi_i = \{0\}$ $(i=1,2)$, while $\eta\phi_1=1$, $\eta\phi_2=0$. Then $\nu\phi_1 = \nu\phi_2$, but nevertheless $\phi_1 \neq \phi_2$. Consequently ν is not an epimorphism.

Other categories in which epimorphisms need not be epi are K(SGU) and K(DLa), and their subcategories K(SGU, θ) and K(DLa, θ), $\theta \in$ ORD. K. DRBOHLAV [30] has shown this by an example for K(SGU) and the K(SGU, θ); below we give an example of an epimorphism in K(DLa) that is not onto. This example can easily be adapted to show that each category K(DLa, θ), $\theta \in$ ORD, contains epimorphisms that are not onto maps.

1.2.7. EXAMPLE. Let $A = \{a,b,c,d\}$ be a four-element boolean algebra (a being its zero element and d its unit), and let B be the sublattice $\{a,b,d\}$ of A. Then B is a distributive lattice; let ν be the identity map $B \to A$. Then ν is not onto, but nevertheless ν is an epimorphism of K(DLa).

For let $\phi_i : A \to C$ (i=1,2) be lattice homomorphisms of A into a distributive lattice C such that $\nu\phi_1 = \nu\phi_2$. Then $x\phi_1 = x\phi_2$ for all $x \in A \setminus \{c\}$. Let $a\phi_1 = \bar{a}$ $(=a\phi_2)$, $b\phi_1 = \bar{b}$ $(=b\phi_2)$, $d\phi_1 = \bar{d}$ $(=d\phi_2)$; $c\phi_1 = \bar{c}_1$, $c\phi_2 = \bar{c}_2$. As $b \cup c = d$, $b \cap c = a$ we must have

(1) $$\bar{b} \cup \bar{c}_1 = \bar{b} \cup \bar{c}_2 = \bar{d};$$

(2) $$\bar{b} \cap \bar{c}_1 = \bar{b} \cap \bar{c}_2 = \bar{a}.$$

<u>Case 1</u>: $\bar{b} = \bar{d}$. Then $\bar{c}_1 \leqq \bar{b}$ and $\bar{c}_2 \leqq \bar{b}$ (by (1)), and hence $\bar{c}_1 = \bar{c}_2$ $(=\bar{a})$, by (2).

<u>Case 2</u>: $\bar{b} = \bar{a}$. Then $\bar{b} \leqq \bar{c}_1$, $\bar{b} \leqq \bar{c}_2$, and we find: $\bar{c}_1 = \bar{c}_2 = \bar{d}$.

<u>Case 3</u>: $\bar{b} \neq \bar{a}$, $\bar{b} \neq \bar{d}$. As $\bar{a} < \bar{b} < \bar{d}$ it follows from (1) and (2) that $\bar{a} < \bar{c}_i < \bar{d}$, $\bar{b} \neq \bar{c}_i$ (i=1,2). Hence $\bar{c}_1 = \bar{c}_2$, as else D would contain a sublattice with diagram (3), which is impossible as D is distributive.

(3)

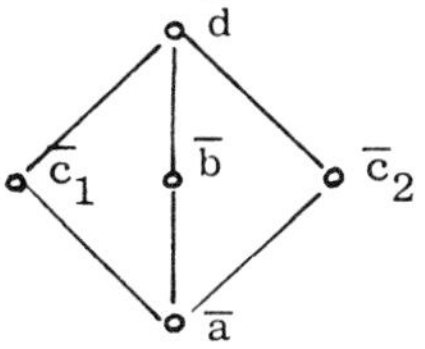

Hence in any case $\bar{c}_1 = \bar{c}_2$; i.e. $\phi_1 = \phi_2$.

In all other categories of 1.2.1 epimorphisms are always onto:

1.2.8. PROPOSITION. **Let K be one of the categories K(S), K(LO), K(PO), K(La), K(BA), K(G), K(AG), K(CZ), K(H), K(CMAG), K(CMoG); K(S,θ),...K(AG,θ), K^{θ}(CZ), K^{θ}(H) (θ ∈ ORD). Then the epimorphisms of K are exactly the morphisms that are onto maps.**

PROOF. Clearly every morphism that is onto is an epimorphism. Suppose now the morphism $\nu : a \to b$ of K is not onto, and let $\xi \in b \setminus a\nu$.

If K is one of the categories K(S) or K(S,θ), K contains a morphism $\phi_1 : b \to b$ such that $b\phi_1 \subset a\nu$ while $\phi_1 | a\nu = i_b | a\nu$. Let $\phi_2 = i_b$.

Then $\nu\phi_1 = \nu\phi_2$ while $\phi_1 \neq \phi_2$; hence ν is not an epimorphism.

If K is one of the categories K(LO), K(PO); K(LO,θ), K(PO,θ), then K admits as an object the (partially) ordered set c obtained from b by "doubling up" the element ξ: $c = (b \setminus \{\xi\}) \cup \{\eta_1, \eta_2\}$, where $\eta_1 \neq \eta_2$, $\eta_1 \notin b$, $\eta_2 \notin b$, and where $\eta_1 < \eta_2 < \eta$ if $\eta \in b \cap c$ and $\eta > \xi$, while $\eta < \eta_1 < \eta_2$ if $\eta \in b \cap c$ and $\eta < \xi$. Moreover, K contains morphisms $\phi_1, \phi_2 : b \to c$ that coincide with i_b on $b \cap c$ while $\xi\phi_i = \eta_i$ $(i=1,2)$. Then $\phi_1 \neq \phi_2$ although $\nu\phi_1 = \nu\phi_2$.

If K is one of the categories K(AG), K(AG,θ), then $a\nu$ is a normal subgroup of b. Let ϕ_1 be the canonical homomorphism of b onto the factor group $b/a\nu$, and let ϕ_2 map b onto the neutral element of $b/a\nu$. Then $\phi_1 \neq \phi_2$ whereas $\nu\phi_1 = \nu\phi_2$.

If K is one of the categories K(G) or K(G,θ), let c be a free product of disjoint copies of b, amalgamating the subgroups corresponding to $a\nu$. Then there exist distinct morphisms $\phi_1, \phi_2 : b \to c$ such that $\nu\phi_1 = \nu\phi_2$; thus ν is not an epimorphism. If K is one of the categories K(BA) or K(BA,θ) we proceed along similar lines, using lemma 1.2.9 below.

Let K be one of the categories K(La) or K(La,θ), $\theta \in$ ORD. Then K admits as an object a lattice c such that $b \cap c = a\nu$ and such that there exists an isomorphism σ of b onto c which is the identiy map on the common part $a\nu$. According to B. JÓNSSON [61], there exists an amalgam d of b and c. Let $\phi_1 : b \to d$ be the identity map and let $\phi_2 : b \to d$ coincide on b with σ. Then $\nu\phi_1 = \nu\phi_2$ although $\phi_1 \neq \phi_2$.

Finally let K be one of the categories K(CMAG), K(CMoG), K(CZ), K(H); K^θ(CZ), K^θ(H) ($\theta \in$ ORD). As in the proof of proposition 1.2.6 one shows that the image $a\nu$ of an epimorphism $\nu : a \to b$ must be dense in b. As $a\nu$ is also either complete or compact, it follows that $a\nu = b$, i.e. that ν is onto.

We used the fact that for boolean algebras, just as is the case for groups, free products with amalgamated subalgebras exist. In fact, we need only a slightly weaker result:

1.2.9. LEMMA. Let A and B be two boolean algebras, and let $A \cap B$ be a subalgebra both of A and of B. Then there exists a boolean algebra C, containing A and B as subalgebras, which is generated by $A \cup B$.

This follows from the much stronger results of PH. DWINGER and F.M. YAQUB [32] .

1.3. Categories of relational systems

The results in the second chapter concerning the existence of certain special morphisms (universal morphisms) in categories mentioned in 1.2.1 presuppose knowledge about universal objects in these categories. The existence of universal objects in the categories listed in 1.2.1 will be discussed in the next section; as in this discussion we will make use of a theorem of B. JÓNSSON on relational systems, we first introduce, in the present section, the relevant concepts. The material of this section is mainly taken from B. JÓNSSON [61] (slightly adapted, however, to our purposes).

1.3.1. DEFINITION. A concrete category K will be called a category of relational systems if all objects of K are relational systems of the same similarity type, and if all morphisms of K are homomorphisms between these systems.

We recall that a relational system is a sequence

$$\mathfrak{A} = (A, R_o, R_1, \ldots, R_{n-1}) \tag{1}$$

such that A is a non-empty set, $n \in N$, $R_o, R_1, \ldots, R_{n-1}$ are relations, and each relation R_i is included in A^{k_i}, for some $k_i \in N$ (in other words, R_i is a k_i-ary relation in A). The sequence $(k_o, k_1, \ldots, k_{n-1})$ is called the similarity type of $\mathfrak{A}$. Two relational systems are called similar if they have the same similarity type.

A homomorphism ϕ of a relational system $\mathfrak{A}$ as in (1) into a similar system

$$\mathfrak{B} = (B, S_o, S_1, \ldots, S_{n-1}) \tag{2}$$

is a map of A into B with the following property: for every i, $0 \leq i \leq n-1$, and for every $(a_1, a_2, \ldots, a_{k_i}) \in R_i$, we have $(a_1\phi, a_2\phi, \ldots, a_{k_i}\phi) \in S_i$. An isomorphism of $\mathfrak{A}$ onto $\mathfrak{B}$ is a 1-1 homomorphism ϕ of $\mathfrak{A}$ onto $\mathfrak{B}$ with the additional property that ϕ^{-1} is also a homomorphism of $\mathfrak{B}$ onto $\mathfrak{A}$.

Examples of categories of relational systems are the categories K(LO), K(PO), K(La), K(BA), K(SGU), K(G) and K(AG) and their subcategories, and also K(H), K(CMAG), K(CMoG).

1.3.2. DEFINITION. Let $\mathfrak{A}$ be a relational system, given by (1), with similarity type $(k_o, k_1, \ldots, k_{n-1})$, and let B be a non-empty subset of A. The system

(3) $$(B, R_o \cap B^{k_o}, R_1 \cap B^{k_1}, \ldots, R_{n-1} \cap B^{k_{n-1}})$$

is called the restriction of $\mathfrak{A}$ to B; in symbols: $\mathfrak{A}|B$. If $\mathfrak{B} = \mathfrak{A}|B$ for some non-empty subset B of A, $\mathfrak{B}$ is said to be a subsystem of $\mathfrak{A}$, and $\mathfrak{A}$ is called an extension of $\mathfrak{B}$; in symbols: $\mathfrak{B} \prec \mathfrak{A}$.

1.3.3. DEFINITION. If $\mathfrak{A}$ and $\mathfrak{B}$ are similar relational systems, given by (1) and (2), and if $A \cap B \neq \emptyset$, then $\mathfrak{A} \cap \mathfrak{B}$ denotes the relational system

(4) $$\mathfrak{A} \cap \mathfrak{B} = (A \cap B, R_o \cap S_o, R_1 \cap S_1, \ldots, R_{n-1} \cap S_{n-1}).$$

If θ is a positive ordinal number, and if similar systems

(5) $$\mathfrak{A}_\kappa = (A_\kappa, R_{\kappa,o}, R_{\kappa,1}, \ldots, R_{\kappa,n-1})$$

are associated with all ordinals $\kappa < \theta$, then

(6) $$\bigcup_{\kappa<\theta} \mathfrak{A}_\kappa = \left(\bigcup_{\kappa<\theta} A_\kappa, \bigcup_{\kappa<\theta} R_{\kappa,o}, \bigcup_{\kappa<\theta} R_{\kappa,1}, \ldots, \bigcup_{\kappa<\theta} R_{\kappa,n-1} \right).$$

1.3.4. PROPOSITION. Let $\mathfrak{A}$ and $\mathfrak{B}$ be similar relational systems, as given by (1) and (2), and let $A \cap B \neq \emptyset$. Then

(7) $$\mathfrak{A} \cap \mathfrak{B} \prec \mathfrak{A} \text{ and } \mathfrak{A} \cap \mathfrak{B} \prec \mathfrak{B} \Longleftrightarrow \mathfrak{A}|(A \cap B) = \mathfrak{B}|(A \cap B).$$

1.3.5. PROPOSITION. Let $0 < \theta \in$ ORD, and let similar relational systems $\mathfrak{A}_\kappa$, as given by (5), be associated with all ordinals $\kappa<\theta$. Furthermore, let $\mathfrak{A}_{\kappa_1} \prec \mathfrak{A}_{\kappa_2}$ whenever $\kappa_1 < \kappa_2 < \theta$. Then

(8) $$\mathfrak{A}_\kappa \prec \bigcup_{\lambda<\theta} \mathfrak{A}_\lambda$$

for all $\kappa < \theta$.

1.3.6. PROPOSITION. Each of the categories K(LO), K(PO), K(La), K(DLa), K(BA), K(SGU), K(G), K(AG), K(H), K(CMAG) and K(CMoG) satisfies the following conditions:

I. Every monomorphism $\mu : \mathfrak{A} \to \mathfrak{B}$ of K maps $\mathfrak{A}$ isomorphically onto a subsystem of $\mathfrak{B}$.

II. There exist objects $\mathfrak{A}$, $\mathfrak{B}$ of K such that $\mathfrak{A}$ and $\mathfrak{B}$ are not isomorphic.

III. If $\mathfrak{A}$ is an object of K and if the relational system $\mathfrak{B}$ is isomorphic to $\mathfrak{A}$, then $\mathfrak{B}$ is also an object of K.

IV. For every two objects $\mathfrak{A}$, $\mathfrak{B}$ of K there exists an object $\mathfrak{C}$ of K such that $\mathfrak{A}$ and $\mathfrak{B}$ are isomorphic to subsystems of $\mathfrak{C}$.

V. If θ is a positive ordinal number, if $\mathfrak{A}_\kappa$ is an object of K for every $\kappa < \theta$, and if $\mathfrak{A}_{\kappa_1} \prec \mathfrak{A}_{\kappa_2}$ whenever $\kappa_1 < \kappa_2 < \theta$, then $\bigcup_{\kappa<\theta} \mathfrak{A}_\kappa$ is an object of K.

PROOF. The validity of I is a consequence of proposition 1.2.4. The other four conditions are clearly satisfied in all cases.

1.3.7. There are still other conditions on categories of relational systems that are important for our purposes. They read as follows.

VI. If $\mathfrak{A}$ and $\mathfrak{B}$ are objects of K such that $\mathfrak{A} \cap \mathfrak{B} \prec \mathfrak{A}$ $\mathfrak{A} \cap \mathfrak{B} \prec \mathfrak{B}$, there exists an object $\mathfrak{C}$ of K such that $\mathfrak{A} \prec \mathfrak{C}$ and $\mathfrak{B} \prec \mathfrak{C}$.

VII$_\theta$. If $\mathfrak{A}$ is an object of K, $\mathfrak{B} \prec \mathfrak{A}$ and card (B) $< \aleph_\theta$, there exists an object $\mathfrak{C}$ of K such that $\mathfrak{B} \prec \mathfrak{C} \prec \mathfrak{A}$ and card (C) $< \aleph_\theta$ (here B and C denote the sets underlying $\mathfrak{B}$ and $\mathfrak{C}$, respectively).

We take the opportunity to introduce here still another type of condition, relevant for arbitrary categories:

VIII$_\theta$. If a is an arbitrary object of K, and if A is a set with card (A) $= \aleph_\theta$, then $\Delta(a,A) \neq \emptyset$ (cf. definition 1.1.11).

The next two propositions are proved in B. JÓNSSON [61] :

1.3.8. PROPOSITION. Let K be a category of relational systems, and let $\theta \in$ ORD. If K satisfies the conditions V and VII_θ of 1.3.6 and 1.3.7, then K satisfies condition VII_κ for every ordinal number $\kappa > \theta$.

1.3.9. PROPOSITION. Condition VI is satisfied in K(PO), K(La), K(G), K(AG), but not in K(SGU) or K(DLa). Condition VII_1 is satisfied in K(PO), K(La), K(G) and K(AG); in K(PO) even condition VII_0 is satisfied.

Clearly condition VII_0 is not satisfied in K(La), K(DLa), K(BA), K(G) or K(AG), as a finite subset of an algebra of one of these kinds may generate an infinite subalgebra.

1.3.10. PROPOSITION. Both condition VI and condition VII_1 are satisfied in K(BA).

PROOF. The validity of condition VI is asserted by lemma 1.2.6. The fact that condition VII_1 is valid is easily verified.

REMARK. Except in the present section we will be extremely careless, writing A for a relational system $\mathfrak{A} = (A, R_0, R_1, \ldots, R_{n-1})$ (unless confusion is inevitable).

1.4. Universal and dually universal objects

The problem of the existence of universal or dually universal objects of certain types is of long and respectable standing. In this section we only mention results concerning the categories of section 1.2; it is by no means our intention to cover the whole field. A few other results of similar nature are mentioned in the notes to this chapter (section 1.6).

1.4.1. DEFINITION. Let K be a category and K_0 a subcategory of K. An object a of K is called K_0-universal in K (or: universal for K_0 in K) if for every object b of K_0 there exists a monomorphism $\mu : b \to a$ in K. The object a is called a universal object in K if it is K-universal in K.

An object a of K is called dually K_0 universal in K if it is K_0^*-universal in K^*, where K_0^* and K^* are the dual categories of K_0 and K, respectively; i.e. if for every object b of K_o there exists an epimorphism $\nu : a \to b$ in K. The object a is called a dually universal object in K if it is dually K-universal in K.

1.4.2. PROPOSITION. Let K be a concrete category, and let $\theta \in$ ORD. If K admits a (dually) $K(\theta)$-universal object a with card (a) $= \aleph_\theta$, then a is a (dually) universal object in $K(\theta)$.

PROOF. Obvious.

1.4.3. PROPOSITION. $K(S,\theta)$ and $K^\theta(H)$ admit universal and dually universal objects, for every $\theta \in$ ORD.

PROOF. Every set of power $\aleph_\theta$ is universal and dually universal for $K(S,\theta)$. As a Hilbert space H is determined up to a linear homeomorphism by the cardinal number of a basis B, and as a continuous linear operator with H as its domain is completely determined by its values on B, every Hilbert space of weight $\aleph_\theta$ is both universal and dually universal for $K^\theta(H)$.

1.4.4. PROPOSITION. The set Q of all rational numbers, with the natural order, is both a universal and a dually universal object for K(LO,0).

PROOF. For a proof of the fact that Q is a universal object we refer to [56] . We will show that Q is also a dually universal object. Let A be any countable linearly ordered set. The set $A \times Q$, ordered lexigrographically, is order-isomorphic to Q (cf. [56] Ch.4 § 7); let μ be an order-isomorphism of Q onto $A \times Q$. Let $\nu : A \times Q \to A$ map $(a,q) \in A \times Q$ onto $a \in A$; ν is an epimorphism, and so is $\mu\nu : Q \to A$.

*1.4.5. PROPOSITION. $K(LO,\theta)$ admits a universal object, for every $\theta \in$ ORD.

A short proof can be found in [80] .

1.4.6. PROPOSITION. $K^\theta(CR)$ admits universal objects, for every ordinal number θ .

PROOF. The Tychonov cube of weight $\aleph_\theta$ (i.e. the topological product of $\aleph_\theta$ copies of the unit segment [0,1]) is a universal object; see e.g. [64] .

1.4.7. PROPOSITION. The Hilbert space of weight $\aleph_\theta$ is a universal object for $K^\theta(M)$, for each $\theta \in$ ORD.

This theorem is due to C.H. DOWKER [29] . It also follows from the proof of Yu.M. SMIRNOV [96] of the J.-I. NAGATA - Yu.M. SMIRNOV metrization theorem (cf. [96] , remark 1 and part 3 of the main proof). We will need a stronger assertion in chapter 4:

1.4.8. PROPOSITION. Let S_θ be the unit sphere in a Hilbert space H_θ of weight $\aleph_\theta$: $S_\theta = \{x \in H : ||x|| = 1\}$. Then S_θ is a universal object for $K^\theta(M)$, for every $\theta \in$ ORD.

PROOF. This also follows from SMIRNOV's proof in [96], but it is easily inferred from proposition 1.4.7 too. Let H be the Hilbert sum

$$H = H_\theta \oplus R \tag{1}$$

of H_θ and the one-dimensional euclidean space R, and let S be the unit sphere in H; S is homeomorphic to S_θ. Then we embed H_θ topologically in S by means of the inverse of "stereographic projection" with the "north pole" (0,1) as the center of projection.

REMARK 1. Proposition 1.4.8 is not really stronger than proposition 1.4.7, even if this seems to be the case. V.L. KLEE [66] has proved that every infinite-dimensional Hilbert space is homeomorphic to its unit sphere.

REMARK 2. There is a still nicer universal object for $K^o(M)$, namely the Hilbert fundamental cube which, being homeomorphic to the Tychonov cube $[0,1]^{\aleph_o}$, is not only bounded but even compact.

1.4.9. PROPOSITION. The Cantor discontinuum C is a universal object for $K^o(ZM)$, and also both a universal and a dually universal object for $K^o(CZ)$.

Proofs can be found in [70] (vol.I §21 theorem VI and vol.II §37, VI theorem 4).

1.4.10. PROPOSITION. K(CMAG) admits universal objects.

PROOF. The infinite-dimensional torus group $T^{\aleph_0}$ - product of $\aleph_0$ copies of the circle group T - is a universal object (see e.g. [93] theorem 2.2.6).

For many categories of relational systems the existence of universal objects is guaranteed (under assumption of the Generalized Continuum Hypothesis) by the following important theorem of B. JÓNSSON [60,61] :

1.4.11. THEOREM. Let K be a category of relational systems. If K satisfies conditions I-VI and VII_0 of 1.3.6 and 1.3.7, K(O) admits a universal object. If $\theta \in$ ORD, if conditions I-VI and VII_θ of 1.3.6 and 1.3.7 are satisfies in K, and if the Generalized Continuum Hypothesis holds, then K(θ) admits a universal object.

1.4.12. COROLLARY. K(PO,O) admits a universal object.

PROOF. This follows from theorem 1.4.11 and propositions 1.3.6 and 1.3.9.

Similarly we find:

*1.4.13. COROLLARY. K(BA,θ), K(PO,θ), K(La,θ), K(G,θ) and K(AG,θ) admit universal objects for each positive ordinal θ .

About K(BA) more can be said:

1.4.14. PROPOSITION. K(BA,O) admits a universal object.

PROOF. As the Cantor discontinuum C is a dually universal object for K^o(CZ) (proposition 1.4.9), it follows from the STONE duality theory concerning boolean algebras and boolean spaces that the free boolean algebra with $\aleph_0$ generators is a universal object for K(BA,O). (This can also easily be shown directly).

1.4.15. COROLLARY. K(DLa,0) admits a universal object.

PROOF. Every distributive lattice can be isomorphically embedded in a boolean algebra of the same weight.

Similarly we conclude from *1.4.13:

*1.4.16. COROLLARY. $K(DLa,\theta)$ admits for every $\theta \in ORD$ a universal object.

From *1.4.13 and the STONE duality theory we also derive:

*1.4.17. COROLLARY. $K^{\theta}(CZ)$ admits a dually universal object, for every $\theta \in ORD$.

We can assert somewhat more:

*1.4.18. PROPOSITION. For each $\theta \in ORD$ there exists a subspace of the generalized Cantor discontinuum $\{0,1\}^{\aleph_\theta}$ which is a dually universal object for $K^{\theta}(CZ)$.

PROOF. This follows at once from *1.4.17 and the fact that every compact Hausdorff space of weight $\aleph_\theta$ is a continuous image of a suitable subspace of $\{0,1\}^{\aleph_\theta}$ (see [64]).

As we saw, for $\theta=0$ a dually universal object for $K^{\theta}(CZ)$ can be exhibited, namely C (proposition 1.4.9). For $\theta=1$ a dually universal object for $K^{\theta}(CZ)$ has been exhibited by I.I. PAROVIČENKO [89] (assuming the Continuum Hypothesis to be valid):

*1.4.19. PROPOSITION. The space $\beta N \setminus N$ is a dually universal object for $K^1(CZ)$.

(Here N denotes the set N provided with the discrete topology; if X is a completely regular space, βX denotes the ČECH-STONE compactification of X.)

1.4.20. PROPOSITION. All categories $K(La,\theta)$, $K(BA,\theta)$, $K(SGU,\theta)$, $K(G,\theta)$, $K(AG,\theta)$ ($\theta \in ORD$) admit dually universal objects.

PROOF. Let K be one of these categories. If A is a free algebra with $\aleph_\theta$ generators of the same kind as the objects of K, then A is a dually universal object for K.

1.4.21. COROLLARY. $K^{\theta}(CZ)$ admits universal objects, for every $\theta \in$ ORD.

1.4.22. PROPOSITION. K(CMoG) admits a dually universal object.

PROOF. Let T_d denote the circle group T, provided with the discrete topology. Then the character group M of T_d is a dually universal object in K(CMoG) (cf. [58] theorem (25.12) or [93] theorem 2.3.3).

Another way to describe this dually universal object for K(CMoG), orally communicated to me by G. HELMBERG, is as follows. Consider the topological direct product T^T; let a be the element $(t)_{t \in T} \in T^T$, and let M_o be the closure in T^T of the subgroup of T^T generated by a. Then M_o is a dually universal object for K(CMoG); in fact, M_o is topologically isomorphic to M. For the characters of M_o are just the projecting morphisms $\pi_t|M_o : M_o \to T$ $(t \in T)$, and hence the character group of M_o is (isomorphic to) T_d.

The group T_d, being divisible, is a direct sum (restricted direct product) of groups, each isomorphic to the additive group Q or, for some prime p, to the multiplicative group $Z(p^{\infty})$ of all p^n-th roots of unity, n=0,1,2,... (I. KAPLANSKY [63] , section 5,theorem 4). More exactly, if P stands for the direct sum

$$\sum_{p \text{ prime}} Z(p^{\infty}),$$

then T_d is isomorphic to the direct sum of P_d and a continuous number of copies of Q_d (we write P_d and Q_d to emphasize that these groups are taken to be furnished with the discrete topology). It is worth mentioning that the group P is isomorphic to Q/I.

Let D denote the character group of P_d, and S the character group of R_d (here R_d stands for the additive group of real numbers; this group is isomorphic to the direct sum of continuously many copies of Q_d). It follows from the VAN KAMPEN-PONTRJAGIN duality theory that M is the (unrestricted) topological direct product of D and S (cf. [58] theorem (23.22)).

The groups D and S are interesting dually universal groups in their own right, as appears from the next three propositions (proofs of which can be found in [58], §25).

1.4.23. PROPOSITION. D is a dually universal object for the full subcategory K(ZCMoG) of K(CMoG), obtained by restricting the class of objects to all zero-dimensional compact monothetic groups.

1.4.24. PROPOSITION. S is a dually universal compact solenoidal group.

(A topological group G is called solenoidal if it contains a dense 1-parameter subgroup; H. ANZAI and S. KAKUTANI [5], after D. VAN DANTZIG [20,25].)

A more exact formulation of proposition 1.4.24 would take the form: "S is a dually universal object for the category K(CS) of all continuous homomorphisms of one compact solenoidal group into another one".

1.4.25. PROPOSITION. The character group of Q_d is a dually universal object for the full subcategory of K(CMoG), obtained by restricting the class of objects to all connected one-dimensional compact monothetic groups.

In other words, the character group of Q_d is a dually universal compact one-dimensional solenoid (the $(\nu!)$-adic solenoid of D. VAN DANTZIG [27]; cf. also [25,26].)

REMARK 3. In [87] it is shown that K(G,O) admits no universal objects.

REMARK 4. It is easily shown, using the VAN KAMPEN-PONTRJAGIN duality theory for locally compact abelian groups, that K(CMAG) admits no dually universal object. In fact, a compact abelian group is metrizable if and only if its character group is countable ([93] theorem 2.2.6), and there exists no universal countable group (remark 2 above).

Similarly one can show that K(CMoG) admits no universal object.

REMARK 5. It is shown in [61] that K(SGU) and its subcategories K(SGU, θ) do not satisfy condition VI of 1.3.7. Hence theorem 1.4.11 can not be applied to these categories. I do not know whether K(SGU, θ)-universal semigroups exist for certain $\theta \in$ ORD. (It is also shown in [61] that condition VI is not valid in K(DLa); nevertheless universal objects exist for K(DLa, θ), as we showed above, using the possibility of embedding distributive lattices in boolean algebras and applying theorem 1.4.11 afterwards.)

1.5. Structure of order-preserving maps between linearly ordered spaces

In one section of the next chapter we need some technical results concerning order-preserving maps. More explicitly, we want to know how an order-preserving map is built up from more simple maps (so-called coherent maps; see definition 1.5.3 below). In this section we carry out an analysis of order-preserving maps as far as is necessary to our purposes. The results below will only be used in section 2.7.

1.5.1. DEFINITION. Let X be a linearly ordered set. If $Y \subset X$, then

(1) $$\widehat{Y} = \{x \in X : y_1 \leqq x \leqq y_2 \text{ for some } y_1, y_2 \in Y\}.$$

If $Y = \widehat{Y}$, Y is called an interval in X. For certain kinds of intervals we adapt the traditional bracket notation; e.g.

(2) $$[y_1; y_2) = \{x \in X : y_1 \leqq x < y_2\}.$$

1.5.2. DEFINITION. Let $\phi \in$ K(LO), $\phi : X \to X$. We put

(3) $$X_{\phi,+} = \{x \in X : x \leqq x\phi\}$$

and

(4) $$X_{\phi,-} = \{x \in X : x \geqq x\phi\}.$$

If $X = X_{\phi,+}$, ϕ is said to be increasing; if $X = X_{\phi,-}$, ϕ is said to be decreasing. The points $x \in X_{\phi,+} \cap X_{\phi,-}$ are called the fixed points of ϕ in X. A left (right) translation is a decreasing (increasing) order-preserving map; a translation is an order-preserving map that is either increasing or decreasing.

1.5.3. DEFINITION. Let X be a set, and let $\phi \in X^X$. The orbit of $x \in X$ under ϕ is the set

(5) $$O_\phi(x) = \{ x\phi^n : n \in N\}$$

and the total orbit of x under ϕ is the set

(6) $$TO_\phi(x) = \{y \in X : y\phi^n = x\phi^m \text{ for some } m,n \in N\} .$$

A map ϕ: X → X is called coherent if $TO_\phi(x) = X$ for some $x \in X$.

The following lemma is evident:

1.5.4. LEMMA. The total orbits under a map $\phi : X \to X$ constitute a partition of X.

1.5.5. DEFINITION. Let $\phi \in K(LO)$, $\phi : X \to X$. Then Δ_ϕ denotes the following binary relation in X:

(7) $$x_1 \Delta_\phi x_2 \Longleftrightarrow (\exists n \in N)(x_1\phi^n \in \widehat{TO_\phi(x_2)}).$$

The map ϕ is called concurrent if there exists an $x_o \in X$ such that $x \Delta_\phi x_o$ for all $x \in X$.

1.5.6. LEMMA. $x_1 \Delta_\phi x_2 \Longleftrightarrow (\exists n,m \in N)(x_2\phi^n \leqq x_1\phi^m \leqq x_2\phi^{n+1})$.

The proof of this lemma is immediate.

1.5.7. PROPOSITION. The relation Δ_ϕ is an equivalence relation in X.

PROOF. Clearly $x \Delta_\phi x$ for all $x \in X$. Suppose $x_1 \Delta_\phi x_2$; say $x_2\phi^n \leqq x_1\phi^m \leqq x_2\phi^{n+1}$. Then $x_1\phi^m \leqq x_2\phi^{n+1} \leqq x_1\phi^{m+1}$; hence $x_2 \Delta_\phi x_1$. Finally suppose that $x_1 \Delta_\phi x_2$ and $x_2 \Delta_\phi x_3$; say $x_2\phi^n \leqq x_1\phi^m \leqq x_2\phi^{n+1}$ and $x_3\phi^{n_1} \leqq x_2\phi^{m_1} \leqq x_3\phi^{n_1+1}$. Then $x_3\phi^{n+n_1} \leqq x_1\phi^{m+m_1} \leqq x_3\phi^{n+n_1+2}$; hence $x_1 \Delta_\phi x_3$.

1.5.8. PROPOSITION. If ϕ is onto, then $x_1 \Delta_\phi x_2 \Longleftrightarrow x_1 \in \widehat{TO_\phi(x_2)}$.

PROOF. Let $x_2\phi^n \leqq x_1\phi^m \leqq x_2\phi^{n+1}$. There are $y_1 \in (x_2\phi^m)\phi^{-n}$ and

$y_2 \in (x_2\phi^m)\phi^{-n+1}$ such that $y_1 \leq x_1 \leq y_2$; i.e. $x_1 \in \widehat{TO_\phi(x_2)}$.

1.5.9. DEFINITION. Let $\phi \in K(LO)$, $\phi : X \to X$. The Δ_ϕ-equivalence class of $x \in X$ is denoted by $\Delta_\phi(x)$; the set of all $\Delta_\phi(x)$, $x \in X$, is denoted by X/Δ_ϕ.

1.5.10. PROPOSITION. For each $x \in X$ the sets $\Delta_\phi(x)$, $\Delta_\phi(x) \cap X_{\phi,+}$ and $\Delta_\phi(x) \cap X_{\phi,-}$ are intervals in X, each mapped into itself by ϕ. If $x_1 \in \Delta_\phi(x) \cap X_{\phi,+}$ and $x_2 \in \Delta_\phi(x) \cap X_{\phi,-}$, then $x_1 \leq x_2$. Each $\Delta_\phi(x)$ contains at most one fixed point; if $\Delta_\phi(x)$ contains a fixed point a, then $\phi|\Delta_\phi(x)$ is coherent (i.e. $\Delta_\phi(x) = TO_\phi(a)$). If $\Delta_\phi(x)$ contains no fixed point, $\phi|\Delta_\phi(x)$ is a translation.

PROOF. Let $x_1 \in \Delta_\phi(x) \cap X_{\phi,+}$, $x_2 \in \Delta_\phi(x)$, $x_2 < x_1$. As $x_2 \Delta_\phi x_1$, there are $n,m \in N$ such that $x_1\phi^n \leq x_2\phi^m$. As $x_2 < x_1 \leq x_1\phi^n$, it follows that $x_2 \notin X_{\phi,-}$. Hence if $x_1 \in \Delta_\phi(x) \cap X_{\phi,+}$ and $x_2 \in \Delta_\phi(x) \cap X_{\phi,-}$, then $x_1 \leq x_2$. As clearly $\Delta_\phi(x)$ is an interval, it follows that both $\Delta_\phi(x) \cap X_{\phi,+}$ and $\Delta_\phi(x) \cap X_{\phi,-}$ are intervals. As $\Delta_\phi(x)$, $X_{\phi,+}$ and $X_{\phi,-}$ are mapped into themselves by ϕ, so are $\Delta_\phi(x) \cap X_{\phi,+}$ and $\Delta_\phi(x) \cap X_{\phi,-}$.

It follows also that $\Delta_\phi(x)$ contains at most one fixed point, and that $x_1 \leq a \leq x_2$ for all $x_1 \in \Delta_\phi(x) \cap X_{\phi,+}$ and all $x_2 \in \Delta_\phi(x) \cap X_{\phi,-}$ if a is a fixed point of $\Delta_\phi(x)$. We now show that in this case $\Delta_\phi(x) = TO_\phi(a)$. Indeed, as $x\, \Delta_\phi a$, there are $m,n \in N$ such that $a = a\phi^m \leq x\phi^n \leq a\phi^{m+1} = a$.

Finally assume that $\phi|\Delta_\phi(x)$ is not a translation. Let $x_1 \in \Delta_\phi(x) \cap X_{\phi,+}$ and $x_2 \in \Delta_\phi(x) \cap X_{\phi,-}$, and let $n,m \in N$ such that $x_1\phi^n \geq x_2\phi^m$. Then, by what we proved already, $x_1\phi^n \in X_{\phi,+} \cap X_{\phi,-}$; hence $\Delta_\phi(x)$ contains a fixed point under ϕ.

1.5.11. DEFINITION. $\Delta_\phi(x_1) \leq \Delta_\phi(x_2) \Longleftrightarrow (\exists y_1 \in \Delta_\phi(x_1))(\exists y_2 \in \Delta_\phi(x_2))(y_1 \leq y_2)$.

In other words:

$$\Delta_\phi(x_1) < \Delta_\phi(x_2) \Longleftrightarrow (\forall y_1 \in \Delta_\phi(x_1))(\forall y_2 \in \Delta_\phi(x_2))(y_1 < y_2). \tag{8}$$

As X/Δ_ϕ consists of disjoint intervals we have at once:

1.5.12. PROPOSITION. The set X/Δ_ϕ is linearly ordered by $\leqq$.

This finishes the first part of our analysis of an order-preserving map $\phi : X \to X$. In order to know the behaviour of ϕ it suffices to have knowledge of the linearly ordered set X/Δ_ϕ and of the concurrent maps $\phi|D$, $D \in X/\Delta_\phi$.

The second part of our analysis will show how a concurrent map $\phi|\Delta_\phi(x)$ is built up from coherent maps $\phi|TO_\phi(y)$, $y \in \Delta_\phi(x)$.

1.5.13. PROPOSITION. Let $\phi \in K(LO)$, $\phi : X \to X$, and let $x < x\phi$. For every $y \in \Delta_\phi(x)$, the set $TO_\phi(y) \cap [x;x\phi)$ is an interval. If, moreover, $y \leqq x$ and $y \notin TO_\phi(x)$, there is a unique $n \in N$ such that $y\phi^n \in [x;x_\phi)$. If in addition ϕ is 1-1 and onto, then for <u>every</u> $y \in \Delta_\phi(x)$ there exists a unique $k \in I$ such that $y\phi^k \in [x;x\phi)$; and $TO_\phi(y) \cap [x;x\phi) = \{y\phi^k\}$.

PROOF. Let $a,b \in TO_\phi(y) \cap [x;x\phi)$, and let $a \leqq z \leqq b$. There are $n,m \in N$ such that $a\phi^n = b\phi^m$; then $x\phi^n \leqq a\phi^n \leqq x\phi^{n+1}$ and $x\phi^m < b\phi^m = a\phi^n \leqq x\phi^{m+1}$. It follows that $x\phi^n \leqq x\phi^{m+1}$ and $x\phi^m \leqq x\phi^{n+1}$. If one of these inequalities is an equality, it follows that $z \in TO_\phi(x) = TO_\phi(y)$. If both $x\phi^n < x\phi^{m+1}$ and $x\phi^m < x\phi^{n+1}$, then $n < m+1$ and $m < n+1$, hence $n=m$, and $z\phi^n = a\phi^n \in TO_\phi(y)$. Thus $TO_\phi(y) \cap [x;x\phi)$ is an interval.

Now assume also that $y < x$ and $y \notin TO_\phi(x)$. As $y\Delta_\phi x$, there are $n_1,m_1 \in N$ such that $x\phi^{n_1} \leqq y\phi^{m_1}$. Moreover, $x \leqq x\phi^{n_1}$; hence $x \leqq y\phi^{m_1}$. Let n be the smallest $m \in N$ such that $x \leqq y\phi^m$. Then $n \neq 0$, as $y < x$, and $y\phi^n \leqq x\phi$, as $y\phi^{n-1} < x$. We conclude that $y\phi^n < x\phi < y\phi^{n+1}$, as $y \notin TO_\phi(x)$. This shows that for every $y \leqq x$, $y \in \Delta_\phi(x) \setminus TO_\phi(x)$, there exists one and only one $n \in N$ such that $y\phi^n \in [x;x\phi)$.

Finally suppose ϕ is 1-1 and onto. Then we can apply the above results to ϕ^{-1}, and we find that for every $y \in \Delta_\phi(x)$ there exists a unique $k \in I$ such that $y\phi^k \in [x;x\phi)$. Consequently $TO_\phi(y) \cap [x;x\phi) = \{y\phi^k\}$.

If $x > x\phi$, similar results are obtained, with $[x;x\phi)$ changed into $(x\phi;x]$; in fact, we need only take into account that if we reverse the ordering of X, then X remains linearly ordered and ϕ remains order-preserving.

1.5.14. DEFINITION. Let $\phi \in K(LO)$, $\phi : X \to X$, and $x \in X$. Then

(9) $$\Lambda_\phi(x) = \{ TO_\phi(y) : y \in \Delta_\phi(x)\} ,$$

while $\leq_{\phi,x}$ denotes the following binary relation in $\Lambda_\phi(x)$. If $\Delta_\phi(x)$ contains a fixed point a, $\leq_{\phi,x}$ is the identity relation in $\Lambda_\phi(x) = \{TO_\phi(a)\}$. If $\Delta_\phi(x)$ contains no fixed point and $\Delta_\phi(x) \subset X_{\phi,+}$, then, for $L_1, L_2 \in \Lambda_\phi(x)$:

(10) $$L_1 \leq_{\phi,x} L_2 \Longleftrightarrow (L_1 = TO_\phi(x)) \vee \vee ((L_1 \neq TO_\phi(x)) \wedge (L_2 \neq TO_\phi(x)) \wedge (\exists n \in N)(\exists y_1 \in L_1)(\exists y_2 \in L_2)(x\phi^n < y_1 \leq y_2 < x\phi^{n+1})).$$

Finally, if $\Delta_\phi(x)$ contains no fixed point and $\Delta_\phi(x) \subset X_{\phi,-}$, we put, for $L_1, L_2 \in \Lambda_\phi(x)$:

(11) $$L_1 \leq_{\phi,x} L_2 \Longleftrightarrow (L_2 = TO_\phi(x)) \vee \vee ((L_1 \neq TO_\phi(x)) \wedge (L_2 \neq TO_\phi(x)) \wedge (\exists n \in N)(\exists y_1 \in L_1)(\exists y_2 \in L_2)(x\phi^{n+1} < y_1 \leq y_2 < x\phi^n)).$$

1.5.15. PROPOSITION. The relation $\leq_{\phi,x}$ linearly orders $\Lambda_\phi(x)$.

PROOF. To simplify the notation we will write Λ and $\leq$ instead of $\Lambda_\phi(x)$ and $\leq_{\phi,x}$. If suffices to consider the case where $\Delta_\phi(x)$ contains no fixed point, while $x < x\phi$.

Evidently $L \leq L$ for all $L \in \Lambda$. Let $L_1, L_2 \in \Lambda$ such that $L_1 \leq L_2$ and $L_2 \leq L_1$. If either $L_1 = TO_\phi(x)$ or $L_2 = TO_\phi(x)$, then $L_1 = L_2 = TO_\phi(x)$. Suppose $L_1 \neq TO_\phi(x)$ and $L_2 \neq TO_\phi(x)$. Let $n, m \in N$, $a, b \in L_1$ and $c, d \in L_2$ such that

(12) $$x\phi^n < a \leq d < x\phi^{n+1}$$

and

(13) $$x\phi^m < c \leq b < x\phi^{m+1} .$$

Then $a\phi^m, d\phi^m, c\phi^n$ and $b\phi^n$ are all contained in $[x\phi^{n+m}; x\phi^{n+m+1})$, and it follows from proposition 1.5.13 that $L_1 = L_2$.

Next suppose $L_1, L_2, L_3 \in \Lambda$, $L_1 \leqq L_2$ and $L_2 \leqq L_3$. If $L_1 = TO_\phi(x)$, then $L_1 \leqq L_3$. Assume $L_1 \neq TO_\phi(x)$; then also $L_2 \neq TO_\phi(x)$ and $L_3 \neq TO_\phi(x)$. Let $n, m \in N$, $a \in L_1$, b and $c \in L_2$ and $d \in L_3$, such that

(14) $$x\phi^n < a \leqq b < x\phi^{n+1}$$

and

(15) $$x\phi^m < c \leqq d < x\phi^{m+1}.$$

Then

(16) $$x\phi^{n+m} < a\phi^m \leqq b\phi^m < x\phi^{n+m+1}$$

and

(17) $$x\phi^{n+m} < c\phi^n \leqq d\phi^n < x\phi^{n+m+1}.$$

It follows from proposition 1.5.13 that either $L_1 = L_2 = L_3$ or

(18) $$x\phi^{n+m} < a\phi^m \leqq d\phi^n < x\phi^{n+m+1};$$

hence $L_1 \leqq L_3$.

Finally we must show that the relation $\leqq$ is total in Λ. Let $L_1, L_2 \in \Lambda$; we may assume $L_1 \neq TO_\phi(x)$, $L_2 \neq TO_\phi(x)$. Take $y_1 \in L_1$, $y_2 \in L_2$. As $y_1 \Delta_\phi x$ and $y_2 \Delta_\phi x$, there are $n, n_1, n_2 \in N$ such that $y_i\phi^{n_i} \leqq x\phi^n$ $(i=1,2)$. It follows easily that $L_i \cap [x\phi^n; x\phi^{n+1}) \neq \emptyset$ $(i=1,2)$; hence either $L_1 \leqq L_2$ or $L_2 \leqq L_1$.

REMARK 1. As $TO_\phi(x) \leqq_{\phi,x} L$ for all $L \in \Lambda_\phi(x)$, in general $\leqq_{\phi,x} \neq \leqq_{\phi,y}$, even if $\Lambda_\phi(x) = \Lambda_\phi(y)$.

REMARK 2. Suppose $\Delta_\phi(x)$ contains no fixed point; let e.g. $x < x_\phi$. Then by logical inversion of (10) we have for $L_1, L_2 \in \Lambda_\phi(x)$, $L_1 \neq TO_\phi(x)$, $L_2 \neq TO_\phi(x)$:

(19) $$L_1 <_{\phi,x} L_2 \Longleftrightarrow (\forall n \in N)(\forall a \in L_1 \cap [x\phi^n; x\phi^{n+1})) \\ (\forall b \in L_2 \cap [x\phi^n; x\phi^{n+1}))(a < b).$$

From this we conclude that $\leqq_{\phi,x} = \leqq_{\phi,y}$ if $y \in TO_\phi(x)$. This remains true if $x > x\phi$ and if $\Delta_\phi(x)$ has a fixed point under ϕ.

We conclude this section with a few remarks on coherent order-preserving maps.

1.5.16. DEFINITION. Let $\phi \in K(LO)$, $\phi : X \to X$, and $x \in X$. Then $E_{\phi,x}$ denotes the following equivalence relation in $TO_\phi(x)$:

(20) $$x_1 E_{\phi,x} x_2 \Longleftrightarrow (\exists n \in N)(x_1\phi^n = x_2\phi^n).$$

We write $E_{\phi,x}(y)$ for the $E_{\phi,x}$-equivalence class of $y \in TO_\phi(x)$.

1.5.17. PROPOSITION. Every $E_{\phi,x}$ is an interval in X. For each $n \in N$ we have

(21) $$(E_{\phi,x}(y))\phi^n \subset E_{\phi,x}(y\phi^n).$$

If $TO_\phi(x)$ contains no fixed point under ϕ, then

(22) $$(E_{\phi,x}(y))\phi^n \cap (E_{\phi,x}(y))\phi^m = \emptyset$$

for $n,m \in N$, $n \neq m$.

The straightforward proof is omitted.

1.5.18. COROLLARY. If $TO_\phi(x)$ contains no fixed point, then $TO_\phi(x)$ can be written as the union of countably many disjoint intervals

(23) $$TO_\phi(x) = \bigcup_{k \in I} E_k,$$

where each E_k is an $E_{\phi,x}$-equivalence class, while $E_k\phi \subset E_{k+1}$, for every $k \in I$.

1.6. Notes

Category theory, as is well known, was created by S. EILENBERG and S. MACLANE (cf. [36] and [76,77]). In our exposition we have chosen as a guide the paper of A.G. KUROSH, A.Kh. LIVSHITS and E.G. SHUL'GEIFER([73] ; english translation: [74]). Most definitions in 1.1, and the proofs of the propositions 1.1.2, 1.1.7, 1.1.9 and 1.1.10 can be found there. A notational aberration is our symbol $\divideontimes$

for free joins; it takes the place of $\prod^*$ in [73] . Notational additions are S(a,T) and Δ(a,T)(definition 1.1.8).

The notion of a strong direct join (definition 1.1.8) is new; it is coined for use in section 2.2. Strong direct joins are not uncommon; in concrete categories they are rather the rule. For in many concrete categories K direct joins are (equivalent to) cartesian products (provided with additional structure: full direct products in categories of algebraic systems, topological products in categories of topological spaces, etc.),with the ordinary (natural) projections figuring as projecting morphisms. Such a direct join $b \in \Delta(a,T)$ clearly is a strong direct join as soon as the set a contains at least two distinct elements.

As mentioned in the "conventions" we intend our considerations to be based on a set theory of the kind of J. VON NEUMANN - P. BERNAYS - K. GÖDEL, maintaining a distinction between the terms "class" and "set". We will refrain from discussing set-theoretic problems raised by category theory; we only mention that axiomatizations of set theory are available that are expressly tailored to fit the needs of this theory (see e.g. J. SONNER [98]).

Although the categories listed in section 1.2 are indeed all concrete, it should be pointed out that most of them are not subcategories of K(S). This is due to the fact that distinct structures can be superimposed on the same set. For instance, consider K(PO). Let $\leqq$ denote the usual ordering in Q, and let $\sqsubseteq$ denote the discrete ordering. The identity map of Q into itself gives rise to distinct morphisms of K(PO), such as the order-preserving maps α and β , where α maps $(Q,\leqq)$ identically into itself, β maps $(Q,\sqsubseteq)$ into $(Q,\leqq)$, while again $q\beta = q$ for all $q \in Q$.

A usable definition of K(PO) whould be the following: the morphisms of K(PO) are all ordered triples $(\mathfrak{A}_1, f, \mathfrak{A}_2)$, where $\mathfrak{A}_1 = (A_1, \leqq_1)$ and $\mathfrak{A}_2 = (A_2, \leqq_2)$ are partially ordered sets, and where f is an order-preserving map of A_1 into A_2. If α and β are morphisms of K(PO), say $\alpha = (\mathfrak{A}_1, f, \mathfrak{A}_2)$ and $\beta = (\mathfrak{L}_1, g, \mathfrak{L}_2)$, then $\alpha . \beta$ is defined in K(PO) if and only if $\mathfrak{A}_2 = \mathfrak{L}_1$; in this case,

(1) $$\alpha . \beta = (\mathfrak{A}_1, f \circ g, \mathcal{L}_2).$$

An isomorphism Φ of K(PO) onto a subcategory of K(S) can then be obtained in the following way. If $\alpha \in$ K(PO), say $\alpha = (\mathfrak{A}_1, f, \mathfrak{A}_2)$, where $\mathfrak{A}_1 = (A_1, \leqq_1)$ and $\mathfrak{A}_2 = (A_2, \leqq_2)$ are partially ordered sets, while f is an order-preserving map of A_1 into A_2, then

(2) $$\alpha\Phi = (g, \{\mathfrak{A}_2\} \times A_2),$$

where g stands for the map of $\{\mathfrak{A}_1\} \times A_1$ into $\{\mathfrak{A}_2\} \times A_2$, defined by

(3) $$(\mathfrak{A}_1, a)g = (\mathfrak{A}_2, af),$$

for arbitrary $a \in A_1$.

The other categories defined in section 1.2 should be interpreted in a similar way; then each of them can be shown to be indeed a concrete category, just as we did for K(PO).

It would have been confusing if we had realized all these exact definitions in the text; therefore we preferred to talk about these categories in a naive way, writing about the morphisms of K(PO) as if they were (order-preserving) maps, and about the morphisms of K(CF) as if they were (continuous) functions, etc.

The fact that in categories of topological spaces epimorphisms usually coincide with continuous maps with a dense image is mentioned by H.J. KOWALSKY [68] , p.251.

The contents of section 1.3 are taken from B. JÓNSSON [61] , with the exception of the results concerning K(BA) and K(DLa) and the introduction of the conditions VIII_θ. Theorem 1.4.11 is taken from the same paper, and so are its corollaries 1.4.12 and *1.4.13 (except the assertion about K(BA,θ)).

The fact that K(BA,θ) admits universal objects for all θ was first proved (under the assumption that the Generalized Continuum Hypothesis is valid) by A. ESENIN - VOL'PIN [38] . Our proof, depending on B. JÓNSSON's theorem 1.4.11 (together with the fraction of the results of PH. DWINGER and F.M. YAQUB [32] expressed by lemma 1.2.9) differs completely from the proof of A. ESENIN - VOL'PIN. The latter makes use of this result in order to derive proposition *1.4.17; he also obtains the following theorem:

*1.6.1. THEOREM. For every $\theta \in$ ORD there exists a compact Hausdorff space T_θ of weight $\aleph_\theta$ with the property that every compact Hausdorff space of weight at most $\aleph_\theta$ is a continuous image of it.

In other words, if K(C) denotes the category of all continuous maps of one compact Hausdorff space into another one, then $K^\theta(C)$ admits dually universal objects for each $\theta \in$ ORD (assuming once more the Generalized Continuum Hypothesis to be valid).

The fact that Q is a universal object for K(LO,O) is mentioned already in G. CANTOR [16] , §9, as is the fact that $\eta\sigma = \eta$ for every countable order type σ. The latter property of η was used by us to derive the dual universality of Q for K(LO, O) (proposition 1.4.4).

F. HAUSDORFF [56] proved that K(LO) always contains K(LO,θ)-universal objects, and that K(LO,θ) contains universal objects if θ is not a limit ordinal and if the Generalized Continuum Hypothesis holds (see also W. SIERPINSKI [94]). This was extended to limit ordinals by N. CUESTA DUTARI [19] and L. GILLMAN [44]. A very short and elegant proof, applicable to both cases simultaneously, has been given by E. MENDELSON [80] .

A. MOSTOWSKI [85] constructed a universal object for K(PO,O). J.B. JOHNSTON [59] proved that K(PO) contains a K(PO,θ)-universal object of cardinality $2^{\aleph_\theta}$, for each $\theta \in$ ORD, assuming that the Generalized Continuum Hypothesis holds. He also showed - under the same assumption - that K(PO) contains a K(PO,θ)-universal object of power $\aleph_\theta$ (and hence that K(PO,θ) contains a universal object) if θ is cofinal with ω. B. JÓNSSON [60,61] extended these results by showing that K(PO,θ) admits universal objects for all θ, assuming once again that the Generalized Continuum Hypothesis is valid. See also R. FRAÏSSÉ [41,42,43] for the case θ=O.

B. JÓNSSON [61] also proved the existence of universal objects in K(La,θ) and K(G,θ), for positive ordinal numbers θ. See also

N.G. de BRUIJN [15] for other embedding theorems for groups. The result *1.4.16 concerning the existence of universal objects for K(DLa, θ), $\theta \in$ ORD seems to be new.

The universality of $[0,1]^{\aleph_\theta}$ for K^θ(CR) was shown by A. TYCHONOV [101,102]. The universality of the Cantor discontinuum C for K^o(ZM) occurs in P. URYSON [105] (theorem 16), and the dual universality of C for K^o(CZ) (in fact, even for K^o(C), where K(C) is as defined above) is mentioned in P.S. ALEXANDROV [1]. The fact that $[0,1]^{\aleph_\theta}$ is universal for K^θ(CZ), for every $\theta \in$ ORD, is contained in the following theorem of N.B. VEDENISOV [107]:

1.6.2. THEOREM. The generalized Cantor discontinuum $\{0,1\}^{\aleph_\theta}$ is a universal object for K^θ(ZH), for every $\theta \in$ ORD.

Here K(ZH) denotes the category of all continuous maps of a Hausdorff space X with ind(X) = 0 into another Hausdorff space Y with ind(Y)=0.

Proposition 1.4.7 follows for the case θ=0 from the classical metrization theorem of P. URYSON [104] for separable normal spaces, in conjunction with the theorem of A. TYCHONOV [100] asserting that every regular Hausdorff space satisfying the second countability axiom is normal. C.H. DOWKER [29] proved that a metrizable space is paracompact if and only if it is homeomorphic to a subset of a suitable Hilbert space. From this theorem proposition 1.4.7 follows in its full generality, in view of the theorem of A.H. STONE [99] asserting that every metrizable space is paracompact.

Proposition 1.4.10 follows from the fact that a compact abelian group G is metrizable if and only if its character group X is countable; this, in its turn, is a consequence of the theorem of S. KAKUTANI [62] asserting that G and X have the same (topological) weight.

Proposition 1.4.22 is essentially due to P. HALMOS and H. SAMELSON ([54] , theorem I), and,independently, to B. ECKMANN ([33] , theorem 4); the first explicit formulation occurs in H. ANZAI and S. KAKUTANI [5] (theorem 12). Propositions 1.4.23, 1.4.24 and 1.4.25 are due to H. ANZAI and S. KAKUTANI [5], anticipated in part by D. VAN DANTZIG [25,26,27].

Some additional results on universal spaces are the following. First, in connection with the universality of $[0,1]^{\aleph_\theta}$ for $K^\theta(CR)$, and the universality of $\{0,1\}^{\aleph_\theta}$ for $K^\theta(ZH)$, the following result of P.S. ALEXANDROV [2] should be mentioned (cf. J. FLACHSMEYER [40] for a short proof). Let $K(T_0)$ stand for the category of all continuous maps of one T_0-space into another T_0-space. Let furthermore A denote the space $\{0,1\}$, provided with the topology $\{\emptyset,\{0\},\{0,1\}\}$. Then:

1.6.3. THEOREM. $A^{\aleph_\theta}$ is a universal object for $K^\theta(T_0)$, for every $\theta \in$ ORD.

A different universal object for $K^\theta(T_0)$ was constructed by A. TYCHONOV [103].

In connection with 1.4.7 (case $\theta=0$) we observe that P. URYSON [106] obtained a stronger result, solving a problem posed by M. FRÉCHET: there exists a separable metric space into which every separable metric space can be <u>isometrically</u> embedded. A very nice example of such an "isometrically universal" space was given by S. BANACH and S. MAZUR, who proved that the space $C[0,1]$ of all real-valued continuous functions on the unit segment, with the uniform norm topology, has the required property ([12] Ch.XI, theorem 9,10):

1.6.4. THEOREM. Every separable normed linear space is norm-isomorphic to a linear subspace of $C[0,1]$.

1.6.5. THEOREM. Every separable metric space can be isometrically embedded in $C[0,1]$.

Some results for non-separable spaces were obtained by W. SIERPINSKI [110,113] and J. FLACHSMEYER [39]. In the set-up of W. SIERPINSKI, the cardinal number of a space is used as a bound for the seize of the space, instead of the weight. Making use of the Generalized Continuum Hypothesis he shows:

*1.6.6. THEOREM. Let $\theta \in$ ORD. There exists a metric space M with card(M) $= \aleph_\theta$, such that every metric space M_o with card(M_o) $\leq \aleph_\theta$ may be isometrically embedded in M.

From this result it easily follows that for every $\theta \in$ ORD there exists a metric space in which every metric space of weight at most $\aleph_\theta$ can be isometrically embedded. J. FLACHSMEYER [39] treats the following explicit specimen. If X is a set, let B(X) denote the metric space of all bounded real-valued functions on X, the metric ρ being defined by

$$\rho(x,y) = \sup_{\xi \in X} |(\xi)x - (\xi)y| , \tag{4}$$

for arbitrary $x,y \in B(X)$. Then ([39], theorem 1):

1.6.7. PROPOSITION. Let $\theta \in$ ORD, and let X be a set with card(X) $= \aleph_\theta$. Every metric space of weight at most $\aleph_\theta$ can be isometrically embedded in B(X).

It seems to be an unsolved problem (if $\theta > 0$) whether there exists a metric space M of weight $\aleph_\theta$ which is "isometrically universal" for all metric spaces of weight at most $\aleph_\theta$ (the space B(X) has the same weight as βX, i.e. $2^{2^{\aleph_\theta}}$). In [39], J. FLACHSMEYER only obtains a partial result: for each $\theta \in$ ORD there exists a certain nice family F of metric spaces, each of weight $\aleph_\theta$, such that every metric space of weight at most $\aleph_\theta$ can be isometrically embedded in an $X \in F$. He obtains a similar result on uniform embeddings of uniform spaces of weight at most $\aleph_\theta$. The arguments which he uses in establishing the latter result, after a straightforward adaption, also lead to

1.6.8. PROPOSITION. For each $\theta \in$ ORD there exists a uniform space X, with the property that each uniform space of weight at most $\aleph_\theta$ can be embedded in X by means of a uniform isomorphism.

2. UNIVERSAL MORPHISMS

2.1. Universal and dually universal morphisms

In this section we define the concepts of universal and dually universal morphisms and bimorphisms (more properly, they are universal endomorphisms or automorphisms); we also introduce universal systems of morphisms. A few elementary facts concerning these concepts are exhibited.

2.1.1. DEFINITION. Let K be a category, and let K_o be a subcategory of K. A K_o-universal morphism in K is a morphism $\varphi : a \to a$ in K with the following property: for every morphism ψ such that $\varepsilon^{\psi} = {}^{\psi}\varepsilon$ in K_o there exists a monomorphism $\mu \in K$ such that $\mu\phi = \psi\mu$. A K-universal morphism in K is also called a universal morphism in K.

(1)

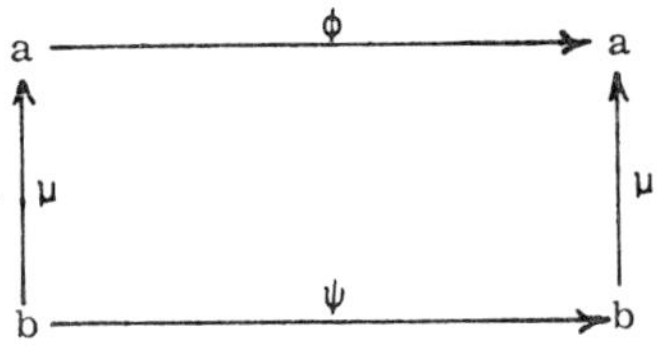

A dually K_o-universal morphism in K is a $\phi \in K$ which is K_o^*-universal in K^*, where K_o^* and K^* denote the dual categories of K_o and K, respectively. I.e. a dually K_o-universal morphism in K is a morphism $\phi: a \to a$ with the following property: for every morphism ψ such that $\varepsilon^{\psi} = {}^{\psi}\varepsilon$ in K_o there exists an epimorphism $\nu \in K$ such that $\phi\nu = \nu\psi$. A dually universal morphism in K is a dually K-universal morphism.

(2)

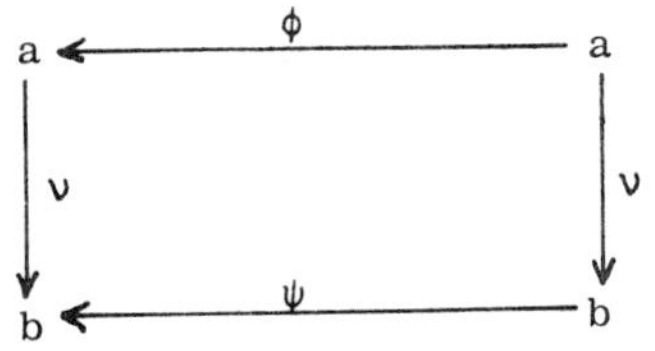

2.1.2. DEFINITION. Let K be a category, and let K_o be a subcategory of K. A K_o-universal bimorphism in K is a bimorphism $\phi : a \to a$ in K with the following property: for every bimorphism ψ with $\varepsilon^{\psi} = {}^{\psi}\varepsilon$ in K_o there exists a monomorphism $\mu \in K$ such that $\mu\phi = \psi\mu$. A dually K_o-

universal bimorphism in K is a bimorphism in K which is a K_o^*-universal bimorphism in the dual category K^*.

Clearly we have:

2.1.3. PROPOSITION. If K contains a K_o-universal morphism or bimorphism, then K also contains a K_o-universal object. If K contains a dually K_o-universal morphism or bimorphism, then K contains a dually K_o-universal object.

Let K be a category. If a subcategory F of K happens to be a semigroup, there must exist an identity $\varepsilon \in K$ such that $\varepsilon = \varepsilon^{\phi} = {}^{\phi}\varepsilon$ for all $\phi \in F$. In other words, F is a subsemigroup of H(a,a), where a is the object correlated with ε .

If we say that F is a *(semi-)group in K*, we always mean that F is a subcategory of K which is a sub-(semi-)group of some $H(a,a) \subset K$, *and which contains* ε_a.

2.1.4. DEFINITION. Let K be a category, K_o a subcategory, and $\kappa \in$ CARD.

A *(K_o,κ)-universal semigroup of morphisms in K* is a semigroup F in K - say $F \subset H(a,a)$ - with the following property. For every semigroup G in K_o - say $G \subset H(b,b)$ - of weight $\leq \kappa$ there exist a monomorphism $\mu : b \rightarrow a$ in K, and an (algebraic) homomorphism h of F onto G, such that $\mu . \phi = (\phi)h . \mu$, for all $\phi \in F$.

(3)

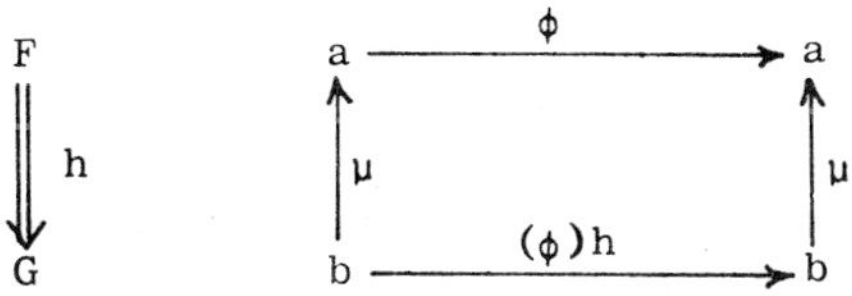

A *K_o-universal semigroup of morphisms in K* is a semigroup F in K which is a (K_o,κ)-universal semigroup of morphisms in K for every $\kappa \in$ CARD. A *(κ)-universal semigroup of morphisms in K* is a (K,κ)-universal semigroup; a *universal semigroup of morphisms in K* is a K-universal semigroup. The dual concepts will be called *dually (K_o,κ)-universal semigroups of morphisms in K*, *dually K_o-universal semigroups*, *dually (κ)-universal semigroups* and *dually universal semi-*

groups of morphisms in K, respectively.

2.1.5. DEFINITION. Let K be a category, K_o a subcategory and $\kappa \in$ CARD.

A (K_o,κ)-universal group of bimorphisms in K is a group F in K - say $F \subset H(a,a)$ - with the following property. For every group of bimorphisms G in K_o - say $G \subset H(b,b)$ - of weight $\leq \kappa$ there exist a monomorphism $\mu: b \to a$ in K, and a homomorphism h of F onto G, such that $\mu.\varphi = (\varphi)h.\mu$, for all $\varphi \in F$. A K_o-universal group of bimorphisms in K is a group F in K which is a (K_o,κ)-universal group for every $\kappa \in$ CARD. A (K,κ)-universal group is also called (κ)-universal; a K-universal group is also called a universal group of bimorphisms in K. The dual concepts are called dually (K_o,κ)-universal groups of bimorphisms in K, dually K_o-universal groups, dually (κ)-universal groups and dually universal groups of bimorphisms in K, respectively.

The following assertion is obvious:

2.1.6. PROPOSITION. Let K be a category and K_o a subcategory; let $\varphi \in K$ be a K_o-universal morphism (a K_o-universal bimorphism; a dually K_o-universal morphism; a dually K_o-universal bimorphism). Then φ generates in K a $(K_o,1)$-universal semigroup of morphisms (a $(K_o,1)$-universal group of bimorphisms; a dually $(K_o,1)$-universal semigroup of morphisms; a dually $(K_o,1)$-universal group of bimorphisms, respectively).

It is not quite obvious that the converse to proposition 2.1.6 is false: the existence of a $(K_o,1)$-universal group (even with a single generator) does not guarantee the existence of a K_o-universal bimorphism.

2.1.7. EXAMPLE. Let $A = I \times N$, $B = I$; let $\phi : A \to A$ be the map transforming (k,n) into $(k+n,n)$, and $\psi : B \to B$ the map sending k onto k-1 $(k \in I, n \in N)$. Furthermore, let $\mu_n : B \to A$ be defined by: $(k)\mu_n = (k,n)$ $(k \in I, n \in N)$.

Let K be the concrete category consisting of all iterates ϕ^k, $k \in I$; all iterates $\psi^k, k \in I$; and all maps $\psi^k \circ \mu_n \circ \phi^l$, with $k,l \in I, n \in N$.

Finally, let K_o be the subcategory of K consisting of all $\psi^k, k \in I$. We will show that ϕ generates in K a $(K_o,1)$-universal group F of bimorphisms, in fact a K_o-universal group, and also that ϕ is not a K_o-universal bimorphism.

Let G be any group of bimorphisms in K_o. Then G is generated by a map ψ^k, for some $k \in I$. Put $(\varphi^s)h = \psi^{-ks}$; then h is a homomorphism of F onto G. As $\mu_k . \varphi = (\phi h).\mu_k$, and as μ_k is a monomorphism, it follows that F is a K_o-universal group of bimorphisms.

But ϕ is not a universal bimorphism: there exists no monomorphism $\mu \in K$ such that $\mu\phi = \psi\mu$. For every monomorphism $\mu : B \to A$ of K is of the form $\mu = \psi^k \circ \mu_n \circ \psi^l$; and if $r \in I$, then

$$(4) \qquad (r)\mu\varphi = (r)(\psi^k \circ \mu_n \circ \varphi^{l+1}) = (r-k+(l+1)n,n)$$

while

$$(5) \qquad (r)\psi\mu = (r)(\psi^{k+1} \circ \mu_n \circ \varphi^l) = (r-k-1+ln,n);$$

for no choice of $k,l \in I$ and $n \in N$ we have $r-k+(l+1)n = r-k-1+ln$, for all $r \in I$.

REMARK. One easily shows that the category K of example 2.1.7 contains no K_o-universal bimorphism at all. Hence it can occur that there is a K_o-universal group of bimorphisms while no K_o-universal morphisms exist. Similarly, there may exist a K_o-universal semigroup of morphisms in a category K which contains no K_o-universal morphisms (this also follows from example 2.1.7). Similar observations can be made concerning the dual concepts.

2.1.8. PROPOSITION. Let K be a category, and let F and G be semigroups in K, say $F \subset H(a,a)$ and $G \subset H(b,b)$. If there exists a monomorphism $\mu : b \to a$ in K with the following properties:

(i) for every $\varphi \in F$ there exists a $\gamma \in G$ such that $\mu\phi = \gamma\mu$;

(ii) for every $\gamma \in G$ there exists a $\phi \in F$ such that $\mu\phi = \gamma\mu$;

then there exists a homomorphism h of F onto G such that $\mu\phi = (\phi h).\mu$, for all $\phi \in F$.

PROOF. If $\mu\phi = \gamma_1\mu$ and $\mu\phi = \gamma_2\mu$, then $\gamma_1 = \gamma_2$ (as μ is a monomorphism). Now for $\phi \in F$ we define ϕh to be the unique $\gamma \in G$ such that

$\mu\phi = \gamma\mu$. By assumption, h maps F onto G, and by definition, $\mu\phi = (\phi h)\mu$, for all $\phi \in F$. It remains to be shown that h is a homomorphism. Indeed, as $\mu\phi_i = (\phi_i h)\mu$ $(i=1,2)$ imply

(6) $$\mu\phi_1\phi_2 = (\phi_1 h).\mu.\phi_2 = (\phi_1 h)(\phi_2 h).\mu ,$$

we see that

(7) $$(\phi_1\phi_2)h = (\phi_1 h).(\phi_2 h).$$

2.1.9. COROLLARY. Let K be a category, and K_o a subcategory of K. Let F be a semigroup of morphisms (a group of bimorphisms) in K. In order that F is a (K_o,κ)-universal semigroup of morphisms (a (K_o,κ)-universal group of bimorphisms) it is necessary and sufficient that F have the following property. If G is any semigroup of morphisms (group of bimorphisms) in K_o, there exists a monomorphism $\mu \in K$ such that

(i) for every $\phi \in F$ there is a $\gamma \in G$ such that $\mu\phi = \gamma\mu$;

(ii) for every $\gamma \in G$ there is a $\phi \in F$ such that $\mu\phi = \gamma\mu$.

A dual assertion is valid for dually (K_o,κ)-universal (semi-)groups of morphisms in K.

2.2. Star functors

If X is a non-void set, every $\phi \in K(S)$, $\phi : A \to B$ gives rise in a natural way to a map $\phi^{**} : X^B \to X^A$, defined as follows: $(x_\beta)_{\beta \in B}\phi^{**} = (x_{\alpha\phi})_{\alpha \in A}$. Mappings like ϕ^{**} often have nice properties; they have been partly studied in [8] . In the present section we consider a generalization of the functor $\phi \to \phi^{**}$ of K(S) into itself.

2.2.1. DEFINITION. Let K be a category, a an object of K and C a subcategory of K(S). A <u>(K,a,C)-lift</u> is a function Ω, defined on the class of objects of C, such that

(1) $$(A)\Omega \in \Delta(a,A)$$

for every object A of C (cf. definition 1.1.8).

Let K be a category and a an object of K. Suppose X and Y are non-void sets, and let $(\pi_\xi)_{\xi \in X} \in \Delta(a,X)$, $(\sigma_\eta)_{\eta \in Y} \in \Delta(a,Y)$. Say

(2) $$x = \prod S(a,X)(\pi_\xi)$$

and

(3) $$y = \prod S(a,Y)(\sigma_\eta).$$

Let ϕ be an arbitrary map $A \to B$. As $\sigma_{\xi\phi}$ is a morphism $y \to a$, for every $\xi \in X$, there exists (by the very definition of direct join, 1.1.8) a unique $\phi^*: y \to x$ in K such that

(4) $$\phi^* \pi_\xi = \sigma_{\xi\phi}$$

for all $\xi \in X$.

Now let Z also be a non-void set; let

(5) $$z = \prod S(a,Z)(\tau_\zeta),$$

and let ψ be a map $Y \to Z$. Writing ψ^* for the uniquely determined morphism $z \to y$ of K such that

(6) $$\psi^* \sigma_\eta = \tau_{\eta\psi}$$

for all $\eta \in Y$, and $(\phi\psi)^*$ for the uniquely determined morphism $z \to x$ of K such that

(7) $$(\phi\psi)^* \pi_\xi = \tau_{\xi\phi\psi}$$

for all $\xi \in X$, we assert that

(8) $$(\phi\psi)^* = \psi^* \phi^*.$$

Indeed, for arbitrary $\xi \in X$ we have

(9) $$\psi^* \phi^* \pi_\xi = \psi^* \sigma_{\xi\phi} = \tau_{\xi\phi\psi};$$

from (7), (9) and proposition 1.1.12, assertion (8) follows.

2.2.2. DEFINITION. Let K be a category, a an object of K and C a subcategory of K(S). Let Ω be a K(a,C)-lift. Then Φ_Ω denotes the uniquely determined contravariant functor $C \to K$ with the following property. If $\phi: X \to Y$ is an arbitrary morphism of C, and if

(10) $$X\Omega = (\pi_\xi)_{\xi \in X}, \quad x = \prod S(a,X)(\pi_\xi),$$

and

(11) $$Y\Omega = (\tau_\eta)_{\eta \in Y},\quad y = \prod S(a,Y)(\tau_\eta),$$

then (φ) $\Phi_\Omega : y \to x$, and

(12) $$(\phi\Phi_\Omega)\cdot\pi_\xi = \tau_{\xi\phi}$$

for all $\xi \in X$. A (K,a,C) star functor is a contravariant functor $\Phi : C \to K$ such that $\Phi = \Phi_\Omega$ for some (K,a,C)-lift Ω.

In many situations there is a "natural" lift Ω, and consequently also a "natural" star functor. This is the case if in K there exist privileged direct joins, as e.g. the cartesian product in K(S), the full direct product in K(G), the topological product in K(CR), etc.

2.2.3. PROPOSITION. Let K be a category, a an object of K and C a subcategory of K(S). If $\Delta(a,A)$ is a non-void set, for each object A of C, then there exists a (K,a,C) star functor.

PROOF. This is an immediate consequence of the axiom of choice.

2.2.4. PROPOSITION. Let K be a category, a an object of K and C a subcategory of K(S) with finitely many objects. If the class $\Delta(a,A)$ is non-void, for every object A of C, then there exists a (K,a,C) star functor.

2.2.5. DEFINITION. Let K be a category, a an object of K, and C a subcategory of K(S). A strong (K,a,C)-lift is a (K,a,C)-lift Ω with the following two properties:

(i) $A\Omega$ is a strong direct join of S(a,A), for every object A of C;

(ii) if A and B are distinct objects of C, then the morphisms in $A\Omega$ and those in $B\Omega$ have distinct sources.

A strong (K,a,C) star functor is a star functor Φ such that $\Phi = \Phi_\Omega$ for some strong (K,a,C)-lift Ω.

2.2.6. PROPOSITION. A strong (K,a,C) star functor is an anti-isomorphism of C into K.

PROOF. Let φ,ψ be morphisms of C such that $\varphi\Phi = \psi\Phi$. Then necessarily $\varepsilon^{\varphi} = \varepsilon^{\psi}$ and ${}^{\varphi}\varepsilon = {}^{\psi}\varepsilon$; say both φ and ψ map X into Y. Let $X\Omega = (\pi_{\xi})_{\xi \in X}$ and $Y\Omega = (\tau_{\eta})_{\eta \in Y}$, where Ω is a strong lift such that $\Phi = \Phi_{\Omega}$, and let the objects x,y of K be given by (10), (11). If $\sigma = \varphi\Phi = \psi\Phi$, then

(13) $$\tau_{\xi\varphi} = \sigma\pi_{\xi} = \tau_{\xi\psi}$$

for every $\xi \in X$; as y is a strong direct join, it follows that $\xi\varphi = \xi\psi$.

It remains to be shown that $\varphi\cdot\psi$ is defined in C whenever $(\psi\Phi)(\varphi\Phi)$ is defined in K. But if $(\psi\Phi)(\varphi\Phi)$ is defined, then the sink of $\psi\Phi$ coincides with the source of $\varphi\Phi$; it then follows from condition (ii) in definition 2.2.5 that also the source of ψ coincides with the sink of φ; i.e. $\varphi\psi$ is defined in C.

2.2.7. PROPOSITION. Let K be a category, a an object of K and C a subcategory of K(S). Let Φ be a strong (K,a,C) star functor. Then for arbitrary $\varphi \in C$ the following assertions are valid:

(i) If φ is an onto map (and hence an epimorphism) in C, then $\varphi\Phi$ is a monomorphism in K.

(ii) If $\varphi\Phi$ is a monomorphism in K, φ is an epimorphism in C.

(iii) If $\varphi\Phi$ is an epimorphism in K, φ is a monomorphism in C.

PROOF. Assume $\varphi : X \rightarrow Y$ is a morphism of C which is onto. As Φ is an anti-isomorphism (proposition 2.2.6), $\varphi\Phi$ is a monomorphism in $(C)\Phi$. We must show that $\sigma = \varphi\Phi$ even is a monomorphism in K.

Let Ω be a strong lift correlated with Φ, and let the objects x,y of K be determined by (10) and (11).

Suppose $\rho_1\sigma = \rho_2\sigma$ in K. Then

(14) $$\rho_1\tau_{\xi\varphi} = \rho_1\sigma\pi_{\xi} = \rho_2\sigma\pi_{\xi} = \rho_2\tau_{\xi\varphi}$$

for all $\xi \in X$. As φ maps X onto Y it follows that $\rho_1\tau_{\eta} = \rho_2\tau_{\eta}$ for all $\eta \in Y$, and consequently (proposition 1.1.12) that $\rho_1 = \rho_2$. Hence σ is a monomorphism in K.

If $\varphi\Phi$ is a monomorphism (epimorphism) in K, it is certainly also a monomorphism (epimorphism) in the subcategory $(C)\Phi$ of K; as Φ is an anti-isomorphism, it follows that ϕ is an epimorphism (monomorphism, respectively) in C.

2.2.8. PROPOSITION. Let K be a category, a an object of K, and C a subcategory of K(S). If Φ is any (K,a,C) star functor, and if ϕ is any invertible morphism in C, then ϕ^{Φ} is invertible in K, hence is a bimorphism.

PROOF. First we consider the case of an identity map i_X, X an object of C. Let

(15) $$x = \prod S(a,X)(\pi_\xi),$$

where $(\pi_\xi)_{\xi \in X}$ is the image of X under the lift Ω correlated with Φ. If $\varepsilon = i_X{}^{\Phi}$, then

(16) $$\varepsilon\pi_\xi = \pi_{\xi i_X} = \pi_\xi = \varepsilon_x \pi_\xi,$$

for every $\xi \in X$; it follows that $\varepsilon = \varepsilon_x$ (proposition 1.1.12).

Now let $\phi \in C$ have an inverse ψ in C. Then we have, if X is the source of ϕ and Y the sink of ϕ:

(17) $$\phi \circ \psi = i_X ; \psi \circ \phi = i_Y ;$$

it follows that

(18) $$(\psi^{\Phi}).(\phi^{\Phi}) = {}^{\psi\Phi}\varepsilon \ ; \ (\phi^{\Phi})\cdot(\psi^{\Phi}) = \varepsilon^{\phi\Phi}.$$

Hence ϕ^{Φ} is invertible in K.

2.2.9. PROPOSITION. Let K be a category, $\mu : a \to b$ a monomorphism in K, and C a subcategory of K(S). Let Ω_1 be a (K,a,C)-lift, Ω_2 a (K,b,C)-lift, and let $\Phi_1 = \Phi_{\Omega_1}$ and $\Phi_2 = \Phi_{\Omega_2}$. If X is an arbitrary object of C, and if

(19) $$X\Omega_1 = (\pi_\xi)_{\xi \in X} \ ; \ x_1 = \prod S(a,X)(\pi_\xi);$$

(20) $$X\Omega_2 = (\pi'_\xi)_{\xi \in X} \ ; \ x_2 = \prod S(b,X)(\pi'_\xi);$$

there exists a unique morphism $\mu_X \in K$, $\mu_X : x_1 \to x_2$, such that

(21) $$\mu_X \cdot \pi'_\xi = \pi_\xi \cdot \mu$$

for all $\xi \in X$. This μ_X is a monomorphism, and

(22) $$\mu_Y \cdot (\phi\Phi_2) = (\phi\Phi_1) \cdot \mu_X$$

for arbitrary objects X,Y of C and arbitrary $\phi : X \to Y$ in C.

PROOF. The existence and uniqueness of μ_X, and the fact that μ_X is a monomorphism, follow from proposition 1.1.13.

It remains to be proven that (22) holds. Let

(23) $$Y\Omega_1 = (\tau_\eta)_{\eta \in Y};\ Y\Omega_2 = (\tau'_\eta)_{\eta \in Y}.$$

For arbitrary $\xi \in X$ we have

(24) $$\mu_Y \cdot (\phi\Phi_2) \cdot \pi'_\xi = \mu_Y \cdot \tau'_{\xi\phi} = \tau_{\xi\phi} \cdot \mu = (\phi\Phi_1) \cdot \pi_\xi \cdot \mu = (\phi\Phi_1) \cdot \mu_X \cdot \pi'_\xi .$$

It follows (by proposition 1.1.12) that $\mu_Y \cdot (\phi\Phi_2) = (\phi\Phi_1) \cdot \mu_X$.

(25)

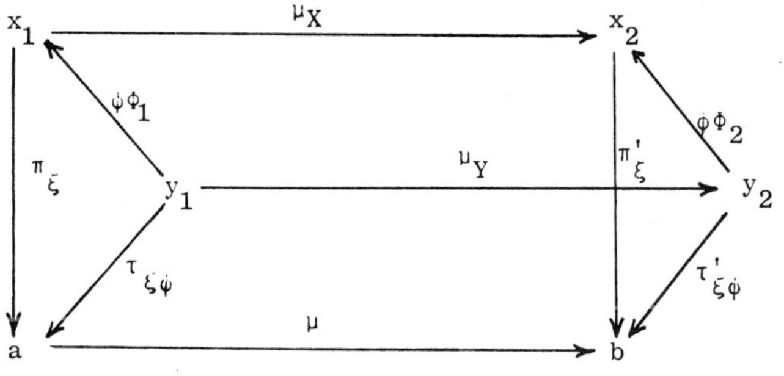

2.2.10. COROLLARY. Let both Ω_1 and Ω_2 be (K,a,C)-lifts. Then the star functors $\Phi_1 = \Phi_{\Omega_1}$ and $\Phi_2 = \Phi_{\Omega_2}$ are equivalent, in the following sense. For every object X of C there exists an invertible morphism μ_X from the common source of $X\Omega_1$, to the common source of $X\Omega_2$, with the following property: if $\phi : X \to Y$ is an arbitrary morphism of C, then

(26) $$\phi\Phi_2 = \mu_Y^{-1} \cdot (\phi\Phi_1) \cdot \mu_X.$$

PROOF. Let $X\Omega_1 = (\pi_\xi)_{\xi \in X}$ and $X\Omega_2 = (\pi'_\xi)_{\xi \in X}$, and let

(27) $$x_1 = \prod S(a,X)(\pi_\xi); \quad x_2 = \prod S(a,X)(\pi'_\xi).$$

According to proposition 2.2.9 there exist monomorphisms $\mu_X : x_1 \to x_2$ and $\nu_X : x_2 \to x_1$, such that

(28) $$\mu_X \cdot \pi'_\xi = \pi_\xi \cdot \varepsilon_a = \pi_\xi,$$

(29) $$\nu_X \cdot \pi_\xi = \pi'_\xi \cdot \varepsilon_a = \pi'_\xi,$$

for all $\xi \in X$. It follows that

(30) $$\mu_X \nu_X \pi_\xi = \mu_X \pi'_\xi = \pi_\xi = \varepsilon_{x_1} \pi_\xi$$

and

(31) $$\nu_X \mu_X \pi'_\xi = \nu_X \pi_\xi = \pi'_\xi = \varepsilon_{x_2} \pi'_\xi ;$$

consequently

(32) $$\mu_X \nu_X = \varepsilon_{x_1} ; \quad \nu_X \mu_X = \varepsilon_{x_2}.$$

Hence μ_X is invertible, with ν_X as its inverse. The equality (26) now follows from (22).

2.3. The fundamental embedding theorem

The main tool that will be used in constructing universal and dually universal (semigroups of) morphisms or bimorphisms is developed in this section. Theorem 2.3.7 below embodies in a very general form the essentials of our construction; the existence theorems of the next section follow easily from it.

2.3.1. DEFINITION. If $\phi_o \in F$, where F is a semigroup, $\overline{\phi}_o$ will denote the map $F \to F$ such that

(1) $$(\phi)\overline{\phi}_o = \phi_o \phi,$$

for arbitrary $\phi \in F$. The transformation semigroup of all $\overline{\phi}, \phi \in F$, is denoted by $\overline{F}$.

2.3.2. PROPOSITION. If F has a unit, the map $\phi \to \overline{\phi}$ is an anti-isomorphism of F onto $\overline{F}$. We then can consider $\overline{F}$ as a concrete category, with F as its single object.

In fact, we will identify $\overline{F}$ with a subcategory of K(S), in the obvious way.

2.3.3. DEFINITION. Let K be a category, a an object of K and F a semigroup with unit. Suppose $\Delta(a,F) \neq \emptyset$. Every direct join $(\pi_\phi)_{\phi \in F} \in \Delta(a,F)$ determines uniquely a $(K,a,\overline{F})$-lift, and hence also a $(K,a,\overline{F})$ star functor $\Phi : \overline{F} \to K$. If x is the common source of the morphisms π_ϕ, we will denote by $STAR_{K,F,x}$ the map $F \to K$, sending $\phi \in F$ onto $\overline{\phi}\Phi$.

The notation $STAR_{K,F,x}$ is ambiguous, as one and the same object x may serve as common source for several direct joins in $\Delta(a,F)$. However, all (K,a,F) star functors, obtained from these direct joins, are equivalent, and hence it does not matter much which particular $STAR_{K,F,x}$ is being considered (as long as it stays the same in each connected piece of argument).

If it is clear from the context which K,a and F are meant, we will simply write φ^* instead of $(\varphi)STAR_{K,F,x}$; ϕ^* is determined by the equations

$$\varphi^* \cdot \pi_\psi = \pi_{\phi\psi} \tag{2}$$

(ψ arbitrary in F).

2.3.4. PROPOSITION. $STAR_{K,F,x}$ is a homomorphism of F into H(x,x). If $\pi_{\phi_1} \neq \pi_{\phi_2}$ for distinct $\phi_1, \phi_2 \in F$ (i.e. if $(\pi_\phi)_{\phi \in F}$ is a strong direct join of S(a,F)), $STAR_{K,F,x}$ is even an isomorphism of F into H(x,x).

PROOF. The mapping $\phi \to \overline{\phi}$ of F onto $\overline{F}$ is an anti-isomorphism. Each star functor is a contravariant functor. Hence $STAR_{K,F,x}$ is in any case a homomorphism of F into H(x,x). If x is a strong direct join, it follows from proposition 2.2.6 that $STAR_{K,F,x}$ is even an isomorphism.

2.3.5. DEFINITION. Let K be a category, a and u objects of K, F a semigroup with unit; let $(\pi_\phi)_{\phi \in F} \in \Delta(u,F)$, and let

(3) $$x = \prod S(u,F)(\pi_\phi).$$

For every monomorphism $\mu : a \to u$ and every homomorphism f of the semigroup F into the semigroup H(a,a) such that $(1)f = \varepsilon_a$, there exists a uniquely determined morphism $\tau \in K$, $\tau : a \to x$, such that

(4) $$\tau\pi_\phi = (\phi f)\cdot\mu$$

for all $\phi \in F$. This morphism will be called $(f,\mu)EMB_{K,F,x}$. If a=u we write $(f)EMB_{K,F,x}$ instead of $(f,\varepsilon_a)EMB_{K,F,x}$. If it is clear from the context which K,F,x,μ are meant, we will write $\hat{f}$ instead of $(f,\mu)EMB_{K,F,x}$.

(5)

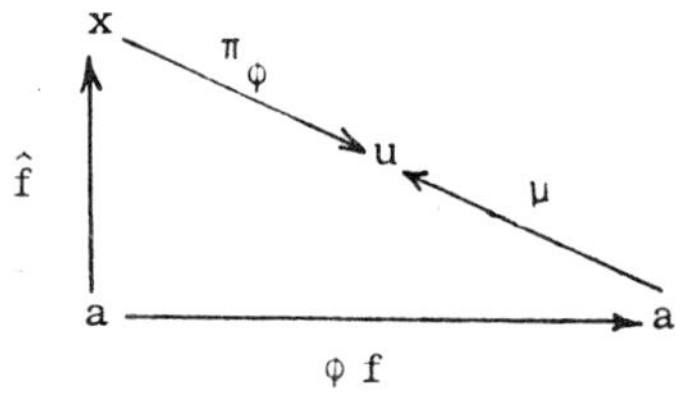

2.3.6. PROPOSITION. Let K be a category, a an object of K, F a semigroup with unit and f a homomorphism of F into H(a,a) such that $(1)f = \varepsilon_a$. Let x be the common source of $(\pi_\phi)_{\phi \in F} \in \Delta(a,F)$. Then $(f)EMB_{K,F,x}$ is a monomorphism of K; moreover

(6) $$(f)EMB_{K,F,x}\cdot(\phi)STAR_{K,F,x} = (\phi f)\cdot(f)EMB_{K,F,x},$$

or, shortly

(7) $$\hat{f}\cdot\phi^{*} = (\phi f)\cdot\hat{f}$$

for all $\phi \in F$.

(8)

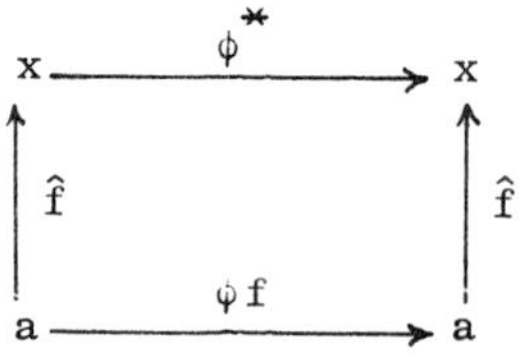

This proposition is a special case of

2.3.7. FUNDAMENTAL EMBEDDING THEOREM. Let K be a category, a and u objects of K, F a semigroup with unit and f a homomorphism of F into H(a,a) such that $(1)f = \varepsilon_a$. Let $\mu : a \to u$ be a monomorphism of K, and let x be the common source of $(\pi_\phi)_{\phi \in F} \in \Delta(u,F)$. The morphism $(f,\mu)\mathrm{EMB}_{K,F,x}$ is a monomorphism; moreover

(9) $$(f,\mu)\mathrm{EMB}_{K,F,x} \cdot (\phi)\mathrm{STAR}_{K,F,x} = (\phi f) \cdot (f,\mu)\mathrm{EMB}_{K,F,x},$$

or, shortly

(10) $$\hat{f} \cdot \phi^{*} = (\phi f) \cdot \hat{f}$$

for all $\phi \in F$.

(11)

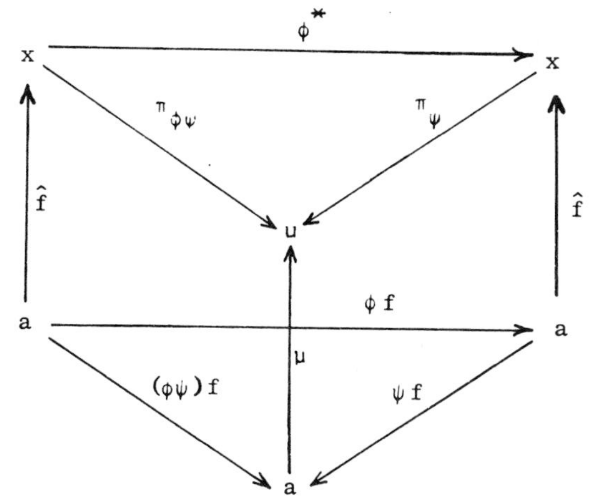

PROOF. First we show that $\hat{f}$ is a monomorphism. Assume $\rho_1 \hat{f} = \rho_2 \hat{f}$. Then

(12) $$\rho_1 \mu = \rho_1 \varepsilon_a \mu = \rho_1 \cdot (1f) \cdot \mu = \rho_1 \cdot \hat{f} \cdot \pi_1 = \rho_2 \cdot \hat{f} \cdot \pi_1 =$$
$$= \rho_2 \cdot (1f) \cdot \mu = \rho_2 \cdot \varepsilon_a \cdot \mu = \rho_2 \mu ,$$

and as μ is a monomorphism it follows that $\rho_1 = \rho_2$.

Now let ψ be an arbitrary element of F. Then

(13) $$\hat{f} \cdot \phi^{*} \cdot \pi_\psi = \hat{f} \cdot \pi_{\phi\psi} = (\phi\psi) f \cdot \mu = (\phi f) \cdot (\psi f) \cdot \mu =$$
$$= (\phi f) \cdot \hat{f} \pi_\psi .$$

Hence $\hat{f}\cdot\phi^{*} = (\phi f)\cdot\hat{f}$.

REMARK 1. If $\Delta(a,F) \neq \emptyset$ one can easily derive theorem 2.3.7 from propositions 2.3.6 and 2.2.9.

2.3.8. PROPOSITION. Under the assumptions of 2.3.7 there exists a homomorphism h of the subsemigroup $F^{*} = \{\phi^{*} : \phi \in F\}$ of $H(x,x)$ onto $(F)f$ such that

(14) $$(\phi^{*})h = (\phi)f$$

for all $\phi \in F$ (in particular, $(\varepsilon_x)h = \varepsilon_a$).

PROOF. Let $\phi_1, \phi_2 \in F$ such that $\phi_1^{*} = \phi_2^{*}$. Then

(15) $$(\phi_1 f)\cdot\hat{f} = \hat{f}\cdot\phi_1^{*} = \hat{f}\cdot\phi_2^{*} = (\phi_2 f)\cdot\hat{f};$$

as $\hat{f}$ is a monomorphism, it follows that $\phi_1 f = \phi_2 f$.

Consequently a map h of F^{*} onto $(F)f$ may be defined by putting $(\phi^{*})h = (\phi)f$. This map clearly is onto; we must show that it is a homomorphism.

Let $\sigma_1, \sigma_2 \in F$; say $\sigma_1 = \phi_1^{*}$, $\sigma_2 = \phi_2^{*}$. As $STAR_{K,F,x}$ is a homomorphism of F onto F^{*} (see 2.3.4), we conclude that $\sigma_1\sigma_2 = (\phi_1\phi_2)^{*}$.

Hence

(16) $$(\sigma_1\sigma_2)h = (\phi_1\phi_2)f = (\phi_1 f)\cdot(\phi_2 f) = (\sigma_1 h)\cdot(\sigma_2 h).$$

REMARK 2. If x is a <u>strong</u> direct join, $STAR_{K,F,x}$ is an isomorphism of F onto F^{*} (proposition 2.3.4). Then we can put

(17) $$h = (STAR_{K,F,x})^{-1} \circ f.$$

2.4. Existence theorems for universal morphisms

The results of the previous section are here applied to obtain a general existence theorem concerning (dually) universal (bi-)morphisms, and similar theorems about systems of morphisms. Combination with the theorem of B. JÓNSSON, 1.4.11, leads to a more special existence theorem for categories of relational systems.

2.4.1. THEOREM. Let K be a category, K_o a subcategory of K, and let $\theta \in$ ORD. If K contains a K_o-universal object u such that a direct join of $\aleph_\theta$ copies of u exists in K, then K contains a $(K_o, \aleph_\theta)$-universal semigroup of morphisms and a $(K_o, \aleph_\theta)$-universal group of bimorphisms.

PROOF. Let F be a free semigroup with unit with $\aleph_\theta$ generators. As $\mathrm{card}(F) = \aleph_\theta$, there exists a direct join of S(u,F); say

$$x = \prod S(u,F)(\pi_\phi). \tag{1}$$

Let G be any semigroup of morphisms in K_o of weight $\leq \aleph_\theta$; say $G \subset H(a,a)$. There exists a homomorphism f of F onto G (such that $(1)f = \varepsilon_a$), as F is free. There exists a monomorphism $\mu : a \to u$ in K, as u is a K_o-universal object. Let $\hat{f} = (f,\mu)\mathrm{EMB}_{K,F,x}$; if $\phi \in F$, we will write ϕ^* for $(\phi)\mathrm{STAR}_{K,F,x}$.

By proposition 2.3.8 there exists a homomorphism h of F^* onto G such that $(\phi^*)h = (\phi)f$ for all $\phi \in F$. By the fundamental embedding theorem, $\hat{f} : a \to x$ is a monomorphism, and $\hat{f}\cdot\phi^* = (\phi f)\cdot\hat{f}$, for arbitrary $\phi \in F$. Consequently

$$\hat{f}.\ \phi^* = (\phi^* h)\cdot\hat{f} \tag{2}$$

for all $\phi^* \in F$. It follows that F^* is a $(K_o, \aleph_\theta)$-universal semigroup of morphisms.

A universal group of bimorphisms is obtained in a similar way, working with a free group F with $\aleph_\theta$ generators; the fact that then the morphisms $\phi^* \in F^*$ are bimorphisms follows from proposition 2.2.8.

2.4.2. COROLLARY. Let $\theta \in$ ORD; let K be a category satisfying the condition VIII_θ of 1.3.7, and let K_o be a subcategory of K. Then K contains a $(K_o, \aleph_\theta)$-universal semigroup of morphisms (a $(K_o, \aleph_\theta)$-universal group of bimorphisms) if and only if K admits a K_o-universal object.

2.4.3. THEOREM. Let K be a category, and K_o a subcategory of K. If K contains a K_o-universal object u such that a direct join of $\aleph_o$ copies of u exists in K, then K contains K_o-universal morphisms and bimorphisms.

PROOF. Let u be a K_o-universal object of K_1 and let F be a free semigroup with unit with one generator ϕ_o. As card(F) $= \aleph_o$, $\Delta(u,F) \neq \emptyset$; let

(3) $$x = \prod S(u,F)(\pi_\phi).$$

We will show that $\phi_o^* = (\phi_o)\mathrm{STAR}_{K,F,x}$ is a K_o-universal morphism in K.

Let $\psi \in K_o$, $\psi : a \to a$. Then if f is the homomorphism of F into H(a,a) such that $(\phi_o)f = \psi$, and if μ is a monomorphism $a \to u$, we know from the fundamental embedding theorem that $\hat{f} = (f,\mu)\mathrm{EMB}_{K,F,x}$ is a monomorphism $a \to x$, and that

(4) $$\hat{f} \cdot \phi_o^* = (\phi_o f) \cdot \hat{f} = \psi \hat{f}.$$

This shows that ϕ_o^* is K_o-universal in K.

The existence of a K_o-universal bimorphism is shown in a similar way, working with a free <u>group</u> F with one generator.

2.4.4. COROLLARY. Let K be a category satisfying condition VIII_o of 1.3.7, and let K_o be a subcategory of K. Then K contains a K_o-universal morphism (bimorphism) if and only if K contains a K_o-universal object.

In some of our applications it happens that a direct join of $\aleph_\theta$ copies of u exists, such that the corresponding object (common source) is equivalent to u. We then can slightly strengthen our results.

2.4.5. THEOREM. Let K be a category, K_o a subcategory and $\theta \in$ ORD. Suppose K contains a K_o-universal object u, and suppose a direct join of $\aleph_\theta$ copies of u exists with a source equivalent to u. Then H(u,u) contains a subsemigroup which is a $(K_o, \aleph_\theta)$-universal semigroup of morphisms, a subgroup which is a $(K_o, \aleph_\theta)$-universal group of bimorphisms, and also a K_o-universal morphism and a K_o-universal bimorphism.

PROOF: evident (cf. diagram (5)).

(5)

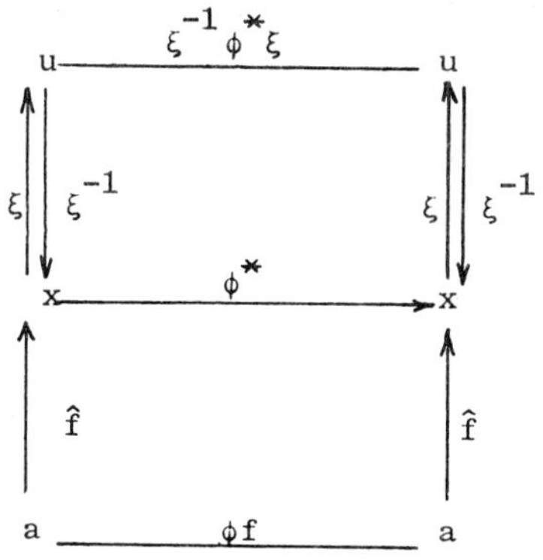

Dualizing, we obtain:

2.4.6. THEOREM. Let K be a category, K_o a subcategory and $\theta \in$ ORD. Suppose K contains a dually K_o-universal object u such that a free join of $\aleph_\theta$ copies of u exists in K. Then K contains a dually K_o-universal morphism φ, a dually K_o-universal bimorphism ψ, a dually $(K_o, \aleph_\theta)$-universal semigroup F of morphisms and a dually $(K_o, \aleph_\theta)$-universal group G of bimorphisms. If moreover there exists a direct join of $\aleph_\theta$ copies of u with a sink which is equivalent to u, then ϕ, ψ, F and G can be taken as contained in H(u,u).

Corollaries 2.4.2 and 2.4.4 may be similarly dualized; we refrain from formulating the outcome.

2.4.7. THEOREM. Let K be a category of relational systems, satisfying conditions I-VI, VII_o and VIII_o of 1.3.6 and 1.3.7. Then K contains K(O)-universal morphisms and bimorphisms, and also $(K(O), \aleph_o)$-universal semigroups of morphisms and groups of bimorphisms. If K(O) itself satisfies condition VIII_o, then K(O) contains universal morphisms and bimorphisms and $(\aleph_o)$-universal semigroups of morphisms and groups of bimorphisms.

*2.4.8. THEOREM. Let $\theta_1, \theta_2 \in$ ORD, and let K be a category of relational systems satisfying conditions I-VI, VII_{θ_1} and VIII_{θ_2} of 1.3.6 and 1.3.7. Then K contains $K(\theta_1)$-universal morphisms and bimorphisms and $(K(\theta_1), \aleph_{\theta_2})$-universal semigroups of morphisms and groups of bimorphisms. If $K(\theta_1)$ itself satisfies condition VIII_{θ_2}, then $K(\theta_1)$ contains universal morphisms and bimorphisms and $(\aleph_{\theta_2})^2$-universal semigroups of morphisms and groups of bimorphisms.

These two theorems are immediate consequences of theorem 1.4.11 and corollaries 2.4.2 and 2.4.4.

2.5. Applications.

Combination of the existence theorem of the previous section with the known results about universal and dually universal objects leads at once to a multitude of universal and dually universal (systems of) morphisms and bimorphisms. Several characteristic cases are treated below. Some of these results are due to J. DE GROOT; see section 2.8 for precise references.

2.5.1. DEFINITION. Let $\theta, \kappa \in$ ORD. We will write $\kappa \lhd \theta$ if and only if

(1) $$\aleph_\theta^{\aleph_\kappa} = \aleph_\theta .$$

REMARK. It is known that the class of all $\theta \in$ ORD such that $0 \lhd \theta$ and the class of all $\theta \in$ ORD such that not $0 \lhd \theta$ are both cofinal in the class of all ordinal numbers; see e.g. [95] (or [11] , § 33.2).

2.5.2. PROPOSITION. $K(S)$ contains $K(S,\theta)$-universal morphisms and bimorphisms, for every $\theta \in$ ORD. If $0 \lhd \theta$, $K(S,\theta)$ contains universal morphisms and bimorphisms.

PROOF. Every set A with $\mathrm{card}(A) = \aleph_\theta$ is a universal object for $K(S,\theta)$. The canonical projections $\pi_k : A^I \to A$ $(k \in I)$ constitute a direct join of denumerably many copies of A in $K(S)$, and A^I is an object of $K(S,\theta)$ if and only if $0 \lhd \theta$. Hence, using theorem 2.4.3, $K(S,\theta)$ contains universal morphisms and bimorphisms for all ordinal numbers θ such that $0 \lhd \theta$.

In the next section we will derive a stronger result: $K(S,\theta)$ contains universal morphisms and bimorphisms for <u>every</u> $\theta \in$ ORD (theorem 2.6.5).

2.5.3. PROPOSITION: K(PO) contains K(PO,0)-universal morphisms and bimorphisms.

PROOF. According to proposition 1.4.12, K(PO,0) admits a universal object. Now let A be any partially ordered set. It is easily verified that the cardinal product A^I - i.e. the set A^I provided with the following partial ordering: if $a = (a_k)_{k \in I}$ and $b = (b_k)_{k \in I}$ are arbitrary elements of A^I, then $a \leqq b$ if and only if $a_k \leqq b_k$ for all $k \in I$ - is the source of a direct join of denumerably many copies of A in K(PO) (under the canonical projections). The assertion now follows, in view of theorem 2.4.3.

In the same way it is shown, using proposition *1.4.13 instead of 1.4.12:

*2.5.4. PROPOSITION. For each $\theta \in$ ORD, K(PO) contains K(PO,θ)-universal morphisms and bimorphisms. If in addition $0 \lhd \theta$, then K(PO,θ) contains universal morphisms and bimorphisms.

2.5.5. PROPOSITION. K(BA) contains K(BA,0)-universal morphisms and bimorphisms; K(DLa) contains K(DLa,0)-universal morphisms and bimorphisms.

PROOF. Both categories contain universal objects, and direct joins always exist in them.

More explicitly, let A be a free boolean algebra with $\aleph_0$ generators. In A^I, define the boolean operations pointwise; then A^I is a boolean algebra, and it is the source of a direct join of $\aleph_0$ copies of A. The boolean automorphism Φ of A^I, defined as follows: if $a = (a_k)_{k \in I} \in A^I$, then $a\Phi = b = (b_k)_{k \in I}$, where $b_k = a_{k+1}$ for all $k \in I$, is a universal bimorphism both in K(BA,0) and in K(DLa,0). Similarly the following boolean endomorphism ψ of A^N is a universal morphism both for K(DLa,0) and K(BA,0): if $a = (a_n)_{n \in N} \in A^N$, then $(a)\Psi = b = (b_n)_{n \in N}$, with $b_n = a_{n+1}$ for all $n \in N$.

Similarly we find, using proposition *1.4.13:

*2.5.6. THEOREM. If $0 < \theta \in$ ORD and $0 \lhd \theta$, the categories K(La,θ), K(DLa,θ) and K(BA,θ) contain universal morphisms and bimorphisms.

2.5.7. PROPOSITION. K(G,0) contains no universal morphisms or bimorphisms.

PROOF. There are even no universal objects for K(G,0)(section 1.4, remark 3).

*2.5.8. THEOREM. If $0 < \theta \in$ ORD and $0 \lhd \theta$, the categories K(G,θ) and K(AG,θ) contain universal morphisms and bimorphisms.

PROOF. According to proposition *1.4.13 there exist universal objects for these categories. Moreover, in K(AG) and K(G) direct joins always exist: as such one can take the direct products (cartesian products with pointwise defined operations). If $0 \lhd \theta$, denumerable direct joins of objects of K(θ) are again objects of K(θ), and it follows from theorem 2.4.3 that universal morphisms and bimorphisms exist.

2.5.9. THEOREM. K^{θ}(M) contains universal morphisms and bimorphisms, for every $\theta \in$ ORD.

PROOF. According to propositon 1.4.7 the Hilbert space H_{θ} of weight $\aleph_{\theta}$ is a universal object for K^{θ}(M). The topological product of denumerably many copies of H_{θ} is still metrizable and has the same weight. Hence, by theorem 2.4.3, K^{θ}(M) contains universal morphisms and bimorphisms.

It is worthwile to formulate separately the result for K^{0}(M), as this can be given a slightly stronger form:

2.5.10. THEOREM. There exists an autohomeomorphism Φ of the Hilbert fundamental cube A which is a universal bimorphism for K^{0}(M). Similarly there exists a continuous self-map of A which is a universal morphism for K^{0}(M).

PROOF. It is well-known that A is a universal object for K^{0}(M) (P. URYSON [104]); as A is homeomorphic to the Tychonov cube $[0,1]^{\aleph_0}$, the denumerable topological product $A^{\aleph_0}$ is homeomorphic to A.

A still stronger result (due to A.H. COPELAND Jr. and J. DE GROOT [18]) will be proved in chapter 4 (corollary 4.5.3 and proposition 4.5.6).

2.5.11. THEOREM. There exists an autohomeomorphism Φ of the Cantor discontinuum C which is a universal bimorphism for $K^{o}(ZM)$, and a fortiori also for $K^{o}(CZ)$. Similarly there exists a continuous self-map Ψ of C which is a universal morphism for $K^{o}(ZM)$ and $K^{o}(CZ)$.

PROOF. This follows from theorem 2.4.5 and the following facts: C is a universal object for $K^{o}(ZM)$ and its subcategory $K^{o}(CZ)$ (proposition 1.4.9), the topological product $C^{\aleph_0}$ serves as a direct join of denumerably many copies of C, and $C^{\aleph_0}$ is topologically equivalent to C.

An explicit example of a universal bimorphism in $K^{o}(ZM)$ is the infinite shift $\Phi : C^{I} \to C^{I}$; if $a = (a_k)_{k \in I} \in C^{I}$, then $a\Phi = b = (b_k)_{k \in I}$, where $b_k = a_{k+1}$ for all $k \in I$. Similarly the map $\Psi : C^{N} \to C^{N}$ such that $((a_n)_{n \in N})\Psi = (a_{n+1})_{n \in N}$ is a universal morphism.

In the same way explicit illustrations for the next three theorems can be constructed; each of these theorems is a consequence of theorem 2.4.5.

2.5.12. THEOREM. For each $\theta \in ORD$ there exists an autohomeomorphism of the generalized Cantor discontinuum $\{0,1\}^{\aleph_\theta}$ which is a universal bimorphism for $K^{\theta}(CZ)$. Similarly there exists a continuous self-map of $\{0,1\}^{\aleph_\theta}$ which is a universal morphism for $K^{\theta}(CZ)$.

2.5.13. THEOREM. For each $\theta \in ORD$ there exists an autohomeomorphism of the Tychonov cube $[0,1]^{\aleph_\theta}$ which is a universal bimorphism for $K^{\theta}(CR)$. Similarly there exists a continuous self-map of $[0,1]^{\aleph_\theta}$ which is a universal morphism for $K^{\theta}(CR)$.

2.5.14. THEOREM. There exists a topological automorphism of $T^{\aleph_0}$ which is a universal bimorphism in K(CMAG). Similarly there exists a continuous endomorphism of $T^{\aleph_0}$ which is a universal morphism in K(CMAG).

Analogous results can be obtained concerning the existence of (κ)-universal semigroups of morphisms and groups of bimorphisms:

2.5.15. PROPOSITION. Let K be one of the categories K(S), K(PO), K(DLa) or K(BA). For each $\kappa \in$ CARD there exist (K(0),κ)-universal semigroups of morphisms and groups of bimorphisms in K.

PROOF. This follows from theorem 2.4.1 and propositions 1.4.3, 1.4.4, 1.4.12 and *1.4.13.

In a similar manner we obtain:

*2.5.16. PROPOSITION. Let K be one of the categories K(PO), K(La), K(DLa), K(BA), K(G) or K(AG); let $0 < \theta \in$ ORD and $\kappa \in$ CARD. Then K contains (K(θ), κ)-universal semigroups of morphisms and groups of bimorphisms.

2.5.17. PROPOSITION. Let $\kappa, \theta \in$ ORD and $\kappa \triangleleft \theta$. Then K(S, θ) contains ($\aleph_\kappa$)-universal semigroups of morphisms and groups of bimorphisms.

*2.5.18. PROPOSITION. Let $0 < \theta \in$ ORD and let $\kappa \triangleleft \theta$. Then K(PO,θ), K(La, θ), K(DLa, θ), K(BA, θ), K(G, θ) and K(AG, θ) contain ($\aleph_\kappa$)-universal semigroups of morphisms and groups of bimorphisms.

2.5.19. THEOREM. K^θ(M) contains ($\aleph_0$)-universal semigroups of morphisms and groups of bimorphisms, for every $\theta \in$ ORD.

Stronger results will be obtained in chapter 4.

2.5.20. THEOREM. K^0(ZM) contains ($\aleph_0$)-universal semigroups of morphisms and groups of bimorphisms. They can be obtained as subsemigroups of H(C,C).

2.5.21. THEOREM. K^θ(CZ) and K^θ(CR) contain ($\aleph_\theta$)-universal semigroups of morphisms and groups of bimorphisms, for every $\theta \in$ ORD.

They can be obtained as subsemigroups of $H(\{0,1\}^{\aleph_\theta}, \{0,1\}^{\aleph_\theta})$ and $H([0,1]^{\aleph_\theta}, [0,1]^{\aleph_\theta})$, respectively.

2.5.22. THEOREM. K(CMAG) contains $(\aleph_o)$-universal semigroups of morphisms and groups of bimorphisms. They can be obtained as subsemigroups of $H(T^{\aleph_o},T^{\aleph_o})$.

We now proceed to a treatment of some dual results.It must be conceded that up to now the harvest is rather meagre.

2.5.23. PROPOSITION. If $\theta \in$ ORD, then $K(S,\theta)$ contains dually universal morphisms and bimorphisms, and also dually $(\aleph_\theta)$-universal semigroups of morphisms and bimorphisms.

PROOF. In K(S) every union of $\mathfrak{m}$ disjoint copies of a set A serves as a free join of $\mathfrak{m}$ copies of A ($\mathfrak{m} \in$ CARD). The assertion therefore immediately follows from theorem 2.4.6.

2.5.24. THEOREM. For each $\theta \in$ ORD, the categories $K(La,\theta)$, $K(DLa,\theta)$, $K(BA,\theta)$, $K(SGU,\theta)$, $K(G,\theta)$ and $K(AG,\theta)$ contain dually universal morphisms and bimorphisms, and dually $(\aleph_\theta)$-universal semigroups of morphisms and groups of bimorphisms.

PROOF. In all these categories free products serve as free joins. As the free product of $\aleph_\theta$ objects of one of these categories is still an object of the same category, and as they all admit dually universal objects, we can apply theorem 2.4.6.

Explicit instances of dually universal (systems of) morphisms and bimorphisms can easily be constructed in all these categories. As an example we describe a dually universal bimorphism in $K(G,\theta)$.

Let S be a set with $\text{card}(S) = \aleph_\theta$, and let G be a free group with the elements of $S \times I$ as free generators. Let ϕ be the uniquely determined automorphism of G such that

(2) $$(s,k)\phi = (s,k+1)$$

for all $(s,k) \in S \times I$. Then ϕ is a universal bimorphism in $K(G,\theta)$.

2.5.25. PROPOSITION. Let $\theta \in$ ORD. If one of the categories $K^{\theta}(CR)$ or $K^{\theta}(ZM)$ admits a dually universal object, it will also contain dually universal morphisms and bimorphisms, and in addition dually ($\aleph_{\kappa}$)-universal semigroups of morphisms and groups of bimorphisms for all $\kappa \in$ ORD such that $\kappa \lhd \theta$.

PROOF. In $K^{\theta}(ZM)$ and $K^{\theta}(CR)$ topological sums play the role of free joins. As the topological sum of $\aleph_{\kappa}$ spaces of weight $\leqq \aleph_{\theta}$ has at most the weight $(\aleph_{\theta})^{\aleph_{\kappa}}$, the assertions follow from theorem 2.4.6.

2.5.26. PROPOSITION. K(CZ) contains dually $K^{o}(CZ)$-universal morphisms and bimorphisms, and also dually $(K^{o}(CZ),\kappa)$-universal semigroups of morphisms and groups of bimorphisms, for each $\kappa \in$ CARD.

This follows from propositions 2.5.5 and 2.5.15 and the STONE duality theory for boolean algebra's and boolean spaces.

Similarly we conclude from theorem *2.5.6 and proposition *2.5.18:

*2.5.27. THEOREM. If $\kappa < \theta \in$ ORD and $\kappa \lhd \theta$, the category $K^{\theta}(CZ)$ contains dually universal morphisms and bimorphisms, and also dually $(\aleph_{\kappa})$-universal semigroups of morphisms and groups of bimorphisms.

However, the following intriguing problem is left unsolved:

PROBLEM 1. Do there exist dually universal morphisms or bimorphisms in $K^{o}(CZ)$?

If such morphisms exist, they can be taken as self-maps of the Cantor discontinuum C; cf. section 3.5.

This almost exhausts our list of "dual applications". We know that there exists a dually universal object for K(CMoG); nevertheless the following holds:

2.5.28. PROPOSITION. K(CMoG) contains no dually universal morphisms or bimorphisms.

PROOF. Suppose $\Phi : G \to G$ is a dually universal (bi-)morphism for

K(CMoG). Let X be the character group of G; X can be identified with a subgroup of T_d.

As the character group of $Z(p^\infty)$ (p an arbitrary but fixed prime) is a compact monothetic group and hence is a continuous homomorphic image of G, $Z(p^\infty)$ must be a subgroup of X. Being divisible, $Z(p^\infty)$ is a direct summand of X; moreover, every endomorphism of X, and in particular, the adjoint Φ' of Φ , maps $Z(p^\infty)$ into itself.

As Φ is dually universal, every automorphism of $Z(p^\infty)$ must be equivalent to a restriction of $\Phi'|Z(p^\infty)$. But every isomorphic embedding of $Z(p^\infty)$ into $Z(p^\infty)$ is onto; it follows that every automorphism of $Z(p^\infty)$ must be equivalent to $\Phi'|Z(p^\infty)$. In other words, $Z(p^\infty)$ would have only one automorphism; this is absurd.

If K(ZCMoG) stands for the full subcategory of K(CMoG) obtained by restricting the class of objects to all zero-dimensional compact monothetic groups, as in section 1.4, we obtain at once as a corollary to the proof of 2.5.28:

2.5.29. COROLLARY. K(ZCMoG) contains no dually universal morphisms or bimorphisms.

The argument used is not applicable, however, to the subcategory K(CS) of K(CMoG) (cf. section 1.4; the objects of K(CS) are all compact solenoidal groups). And indeed it can be proved that in K(CS) dually universal morphisms and bimorphisms exist.

2.5.30. PROPOSITION. K(CS) contains dually universal morphisms and bimorphisms, and also dually ($\aleph_0$)-universal semigroups of morphisms and groups of bimorphisms. They can be taken in H(S,S), where S is the dually universal compact solenoid introduced in section 1.4.

PROOF. As in 1.4, let R_d denote the discrete additive group of real numbers; then S is the character group of R_d. Let K designate the category of all homomorphisms $G_1 \to G_2$, where both G_1 and G_2 are discrete groups isomorphic to subgroups of R_d.

We want to show that in K(CS) a free join of $\aleph_0$ copies of S exists; the proposition then will follow from theorem 2.4.6. Now if G is any object of K(CS), its character group is isomorphic to a subgroup of R_d, hence is an object of K ([58] , theorem 2.5.18); consequently, if $\phi \in K(CS)$, its adjoint ϕ' is a morphism of K.

It is a result of the VAN KAMPEN-PONTRJAGIN duality theory that the operation $\phi \to \phi'$ of taking adjoints is a contravariant functor of the category of all continuous homomorphisms between locally compact abelian groups into itself; it is even an anti-isomorphism. It follows that the restriction to K(CS) of this operation is an anti-isomorphism of K(CS) into K. Hence if we succeed in showing that in K a direct join of $\aleph_0$ copies of R_d exists, it will follow that in K(CS) a free join of $\aleph_0$ copies of S exists.

Consider now the full direct product $R_d^{\aleph_0}$ of denumerably many copies of R_d (with the discrete topology). It is a torsion-free divisible group, hence is isomorphic to the direct sum of sufficiently many copies of Q_d, in fact of continuously many copies of Q_d, as the cardinality of $R_d^{\aleph_0}$ equals the power of the continuum. Thus $R_d^{\aleph_0}$ is isomorphic to R_d and hence is an object of K. But this implies that in K a direct join of $\aleph_0$ copies of R_d exists, with R_d itself as corresponding object.

We conclude this section with two more negative results.

2.5.31. PROPOSITION. K(LO,θ) contains no dually universal morphisms or bimorphisms, for every $\theta \in$ ORD.

PROOF. Let $\theta \in$ ORD, and let K = K(LO,θ). Suppose K contains a dually universal (bi-)morphism $\Phi : A \to A$. We will first prove the following assertion: if a_1, a_2 are arbitrary elements of A, there exists an $n \in N$ such that $a_1\Phi^n > a_2$.

Let B be the lexicographically ordered product $I \times A$, and let $\phi : B \to B$ be defined as follows:

$$(k,a)\,\phi = (k+1,a), \tag{3}$$

for arbitrary $k \in I$ and $a \in A$. Then ϕ is a bimorphism of K. Hence there must exist an order-preserving map ν of A onto B such that $\Phi\nu = \nu\phi$.

Now let $a_1, a_2 \in A$. If, say, $a_i\nu = (k_i, b_i)$ $(i=1,2)$, then putting $n = |k_2 - k_1| + 1$ we find

(4) $$a_1\phi^n\nu = a_1\nu\phi^n = (k_1+n, b_1) > (k_2, b_2) = a_2\nu.$$

As ν is order-preserving, it follows that $a_1\phi^n > a_2$.

Next let μ be an order-preserving map of A onto B such that

(5) $$\phi\mu = \mu i_B = \mu .$$

Choose arbitrary $a_1, a_2 \in A$, and let $m, n \in N$ such that $a_1\phi^n > a_2$ and $a_2\phi^m > a_1$. We see that

(6) $$a_2\mu \leqq a_1\phi^n\mu = a_1\mu$$

and similarly that

(7) $$a_1\mu \leqq a_2\phi^m\mu = a_2\mu \;;$$

consequently $a_1\mu = a_2\mu$. Thus μ maps all of A into one point of B. This contradicts the assumption that μ is an epimorphism.

It is in accordance with this result that it can be shown that no free joins exist in K(LO,θ); cf. section 2.7 for a proof.

2.5.32. PROPOSITION. K(PO,θ) contains no dually universal morphisms or bimorphisms, for every $\theta \in$ ORD.

The proof of proposition 2.5.32 runs in exactly the same way as the proof of 2.5.31.

2.6. Additional results I : K(S, θ).

In section 2.5 it was shown that K(S,θ) contains dually universal morphisms and bimorphisms for all $\theta \in$ ORD. The existence of universal morphisms and bimorphisms, however, followed only for those $\theta \in$ ORD for which $0 \lhd \theta$. We will now give a direct proof of the existence of universal morphisms and bimorphisms in K(S,θ) for all ordinal numbers θ. The results of this section were obtained in collaboration with J. DE GROOT; see [9].

2.6.1. DEFINITION. Let X be a set, and let $\phi \in X^X$. A ϕ-loop in X is a non-void finite subset Y of X such that $Y_\phi = Y$ and $\phi | Y$ is coherent (cf. definition 1.5.3).

If Y is a ϕ-loop of n points, these points can be numbered in such a way that $Y = \{x_1, x_2, \ldots, x_n\}$, while $x_k\phi = x_{k+1}$, for k=1,2,..., n-1, and $x_n\phi = x_1$.

The following lemma is obvious.

2.6.2. LEMMA. A total orbit contains at most one loop.

In the next lemma we introduce certain mappings needed for the construction of a universal morphism.

2.6.3. LEMMA. Let $\theta \in \mathrm{ORD}$, and let X_θ be a set with $\mathrm{card}(X_\theta) = \aleph_\theta$. For every $n \in N$ there exists a coherent map $\sigma_n : X_\theta \to X_\theta$ with the following properties:

(i) X_θ contains no σ_o-loop; if $n > 0$, X_θ contains a σ_n-loop of n points.

(ii) $\mathrm{card}(x\sigma_n^{-1}) = \aleph_\theta$, for all $x \in X_\theta$.

PROOF. First we consider the case n=0.

Let $*$ be an element outside X_θ, and let $S = X_\theta \cup \{*\}$. Let C be the subset of S^I consisting of those $x = (x_k)_{k \in I} \in S^I$ for which there exists a $k \in I$, $k = k_x$, such that $x_n = *$ if $n < k$ and $x_n \in X_\theta$ if $n \geq k$. Define $\sigma : C \to C$ as follows:

$$(1) \qquad (x\sigma)\pi_k = \begin{cases} x\pi_k & \text{if } k \neq k_x, \\ * & \text{if } k = k_x. \end{cases}$$

Here π_k stands for the map $S^I \to S$ sending $x = (x_h)_{h \in I} \in S^I$ onto x_k.

There are no σ-loops in C, and $\mathrm{card}(x\sigma^{-1}) = \aleph_\theta$, for every $x \in C$. But $\mathrm{card}(C) = (\aleph_\theta)^{\aleph_o}$, which will only equal $\aleph_\theta$ if $0 \lhd \theta$. However, this need not bother us, as luckily σ is not yet a coherent map.

We choose an arbitrary $x_o \in C$, and put $M = TO_\sigma(x_o)$. It is easily verified that $\mathrm{card}(M) = \aleph_\theta$, and obviously $\sigma | M$ is coherent. Hence if μ is any 1-1 map of M onto X_θ, we can define σ_o by

(2) $$\sigma_o = \mu^{-1} \circ (\sigma | M) \circ \mu.$$

Next we consider the case n=1.

Let C, σ and x_o be as above, and let

(3) $$M_1 = \{x \in C : x\sigma^k = x_o \text{ for some } k \in I\} .$$

We define a map $\tau : M_1 \to M_1$ in the following manner:

(4) $$x_o\tau = x_o, \quad \tau|(M_1 \setminus \{x_o\}) = \sigma|(M_1 \setminus \{x_o\}).$$

If μ_1 is any 1-1 map of M_1 onto X_θ, the map $\sigma_1 = \mu_1^{-1} \circ \tau \circ \mu_1$ satisfies the requirements.

Finally let n > 1. Let $Y = X_\theta \times \{1,2,\dots,n\}$, and let $\{x_1\}$ be the σ_1-loop in X_θ. We define $\tau : Y \to Y$ as follows. If $x \in X_\theta$, $x \neq x_1$, and if $1 \leq k \leq n$, we put $(x,k)\tau = (x\sigma_1, k)$; if $1 \leq k \leq n-1$ we put $(x_1,k)\tau = (x_1,k+1)$; finally $(x_1,n)\tau = (x_1,1)$. If μ is any 1-1 map of Y onto X_θ, the map $\sigma_n = \mu^{-1} \circ \tau \circ \mu$ is a coherent map $X_\theta \to X_\theta$ with a loop of n points.

We proceed to show that σ_n is a universal map for all coherent maps in $K(S,\theta)$ with a loop of n points.

2.6.4. LEMMA. Let X_θ and $\sigma_n : X_\theta \to X_\theta$ be as in lemma 2.6.3. ($\theta \in$ ORD, $n \in N$). If Y is any set with card(Y) $\leq \aleph_\theta$ and if $\phi : Y \to Y$ is a coherent map with an n-point loop (without loops, if n=0), there exists a 1-1 map $\mu : Y \to X_\theta$ such that $\mu\sigma_n = \phi\mu$.

PROOF.

We present the proof for the case n=0; if $n \geq 1$ the proof runs along similar lines. Clearly we may assume that $Y \neq \emptyset$.

Choose an arbitrary $y_o \in Y$ (if n > 0, y_o must be chosen from the ϕ-loop in Y) and an arbitrary $x_o \in X_\theta$. We put

(5) $$(y_o\phi^m)\mu = x_o\sigma_o^m \qquad (m \in N).$$

Let $A_o = \mathcal{O}_\phi(x_o)$ (cf. def.1.5.3), $A_1 = A_o\phi^{-1} \setminus A_o$, and $A_{m+2} = A_{m+1}\phi^{-1}$, for every $m \in N$. The sets A_m, $m \in N$, are pairwise disjoint, each has power$_m \leq \aleph_\theta$, and $Y = \bigcup_{m \in N} A_m$. We have defined μ on A_o; suppose now $\mu \mid \bigcup_{k=0}^{m} A_k$ is already defined in such a way that μ is 1-1 on $\bigcup_{k=0}^{m} A_k$ and that

$$(6) \qquad y\mu\sigma_o = y\phi\mu$$

for all $y \in \bigcup_{k=0}^{m} A_k$.

If $m \geq 1$, the sets $y\phi^{-1}$, $y \in A_m$, partition A_{m+1} into at most $\aleph_\theta$ disjoint sets (if m=0, we use the sets $y\phi^{-1} \cap A_1$ instead). Let $B \subset A_m$ such that $y_1\phi^{-1} \cap y_2\phi^{-1} = \emptyset$ whenever $y_1 \neq y_2$, $y_1 \in B$, $y_2 \in B$, and such that $B\phi^{-1} \supset A_{m+1}$. For each $y \in B$ there exists a 1-1 map τ_y of $y\phi^{-1}$ into $(y\mu)\sigma_o^{-1}$; we define, for each $y \in B$,

$$(7) \qquad \mu \mid y\phi^{-1} = \tau_y$$

(if m=0, we put instead: $\mu(y\phi^{-1} \cap A_1) = \tau_y(y\phi^{-1} \cap A_1)$). Then μ is defined and 1-1 on $\bigcup_{k=0}^{m+1} A_k$, and (6) holds for all $y \in \bigcup_{k=0}^{m+1} A_k$. The assertions now follow by induction.

2.6.5. THEOREM. The category $K(S,\theta)$ contains universal morphisms and bimorphisms, for every $\theta \in$ ORD.

PROOF. First we prove the existence of universal morphisms. Let $\sigma_n : X_\theta \to X_\theta$ be as described in lemma 2.6.3, for each $n \in N$. Let

$$(8) \qquad A = X_\theta \times X_\theta \times N$$

and let Φ be the following map $A \to A$:

$$(9) \qquad (x_1, x_2, n)\Phi = (x_1, x_2\sigma_n, n).$$

We will show that Φ is a universal morphism in $K(S,\theta)$.

Take an arbitrary non-void set Y of power $\leq \aleph_\theta$, and let $\phi \in Y^Y$. Let C be a choice set in Y, containing exactly one point from every total orbit $TO_\phi(y)$, $y \in Y$; let C_n be the subset of C consisting of all y such that $TO_\phi(y)$ contains a ϕ-loop of n points (contains no ϕ-loop, if n=0). For each n, $\mathrm{card}(C_n) \leq \aleph_\theta$; hence for each n there is a 1-1 map τ_n of C_n into X_θ. Moreover, by lemma 2.6.4, for each n and each $y \in C_n$ there exists a 1-1 map $\mu_{y,n}$ of $TO_\phi(y)$ into X_θ with the property that

(10) $$z\mu_{y,n}\sigma_n = z\phi\mu_{y,n}$$

for all $z \in TO_\phi(y)$.

We define a map $\mu: Y \to A$ in the following manner. If $z \in Y$, say $z \in TO_\phi(y)$, $y \in C_n$, we put

(11) $$z\mu = (y\tau_n, z\mu_{y,n}, n).$$

Then μ is a monomorphism $Y \to A$, and $\mu\Phi = \phi\mu$.

Next we show that there also exist universal bimorphisms. For every $n \in N\setminus\{0\}$, let $A_n = \{1,2,\ldots,n\}$; let $A_0 = I$. We write τ_n for the successor map modulo n in A_n : $(k)\tau_n = k+1$ if $k \neq n$, $(n)\tau_n = 1$. Let X_θ be a set of power $\aleph_\theta$, and let B be the set of all ordered triples (x,n,k) with $x \in X_\theta$, $n \in N$ and $k \in A_n$. We define $\Psi : B \to B$ as follows:

(12) $$(x,n,k)\Psi = (x,n,k\tau_n).$$

Then Ψ is a bimorphism of $K(S,\theta)$; we will show that Ψ is a universal bimorphism.

Let Y be any set of power $\leq \aleph_\theta$, and $\psi \in Y^Y$. The total orbits $TO_\psi(y)$, $y \in Y$, partition Y into disjoint countable sets. Let C be a choice set, containing exactly one point from every total orbit $TO_\psi(y)$; let

(13) $$C_n = \{y \in C : \text{card}(TO_\psi(y)) = n\} \quad (n \in N\setminus\{0\})$$

and

(14) $$C_0 = \{y \in C : \text{card}(TO_\psi(y)) = \aleph_0\}.$$

For each $n \in N$ there exists a 1-1 map τ_n of C_n into X_θ.

We define $\mu : Y \to B$ in the following way. If $z \in Y$, there is exactly one $y \in C$ such that $z \in TO_\psi(y)$, and exactly one $n \in N$ such that $y \in C_n$. We put

(15) $$z\mu = (y\tau_n, n, k),$$

where k is the uniquely determined element of A_n such that $y\psi^k = z$. Then μ is a monomorphism, and $\mu\Psi = \psi\mu$.

2.7. Additional results II : K(LO, θ)

It will be shown below that in K(LO,θ), for arbitrary $\theta \in$ ORD, no direct or free join of two or more copies of an object exists (except in some trivial cases). Thus the methods of 2.4 are fundamentally useless in these categories. Correspondingly, we found (proposition 2.5.31) that no dually universal morphisms or bimorphisms exist in K(LO,θ), for every $\theta \in$ ORD. Surprisingly enough, it turns out that universal morphisms and bimorphisms exist as soon as there are universal objects.

2.7.1. PROPOSITION. Let $\theta \in$ ORD, and let A be a set with card(A) > 1.

Then S(X,A) admits no direct join in K(LO,θ), for every object X of this category which contains at least two elements.

PROOF. Suppose $Y = \prod S(X,A)(\pi_\alpha)$. Let $\alpha_1,\alpha_2 \in A$, $\alpha_1 \neq \alpha_2$. First we show that there exists a $y \in Y$ such that $y\pi_{\alpha_1} < y\pi_{\alpha_2}$ (in the ordering of X). For take $x_1, x_2 \in X$, $x_1 < x_2$, and define $\phi_\alpha : Y \to X_\alpha = X$ as follows:

(1)
$$\phi_\alpha = \pi_\alpha \quad \text{if } \alpha \neq \alpha_1,\ \alpha \neq \alpha_2;$$
$$y\phi_{\alpha_i} = x_i, \quad \text{for all } y \in Y \quad (i=1,2).$$

There exists a morphism $\phi : Y \to Y$ such that $\phi\pi_\alpha = \phi_\alpha$, for all $\alpha \in A$. Then it follows, for arbitrary $y \in Y$, that

(2)
$$(y\phi)\pi_{\alpha_1} = x_1 < x_2 = (y\phi)\pi_{\alpha_2}.$$

Now let $\psi : A \to A$ be the map transposing α_1 and α_2 and leaving all other $\alpha \in A$ fixed, and let $\psi^* = (\psi)\mathrm{STAR}_{K(LO,\theta),F,Y}$, where F denotes the subsemigroup (i_A, ψ) of A^A. Then, if $y \in Y$ such that $y\pi_{\alpha_1} < y\pi_{\alpha_2}$:

(3)
$$y\psi^*\pi_{\alpha_2} = y\pi_{\alpha_2\psi} = y\pi_{\alpha_1} < y\pi_{\alpha_2},$$

implying that $y\psi^* < y$, as π_{α_2} is order-preserving. But similarly

(4)
$$y\psi^*\pi_{\alpha_1} = y\pi_{\alpha_1\psi} = y\pi_{\alpha_2} > y\pi_{\alpha_1},$$

implying that $y\psi^* > y$. This is contradictory.

2.7.2. PROPOSITION. For every $\theta \in$ ORD, there exists no free join in $K(LO,\theta)$ of two or more objects of this category.

PROOF. Let $\mathrm{card}(A) \geqq 2$, and let X_α be an object of $K(LO,\theta)$ for each $\alpha \in A$. Suppose

(5) $$X = \ast_{\alpha\in A} X_\alpha\ (\sigma_\alpha).$$

Take $\alpha_1,\alpha_2 \in A$ with $\alpha_1 \neq \alpha_2$. Let Y be an object of $K(LO,\theta)$ with at least two elements, and let $y_1, y_2 \in Y$ with $y_1 < y_2$. We define maps $\phi_\alpha : X_\alpha \to Y$ as follows:

(6) $$x\phi_\alpha = y_1, \quad \text{for all } x \in X_\alpha,\ \text{if } \alpha \neq \alpha_2;$$
$$x\phi_{\alpha_2} = y_2, \quad \text{for all } x \in X_{\alpha_2}.$$

As all ϕ_α are morphisms of $K(LO,\theta)$ there exists a morphism $\phi : X \to Y$ in $K(LO,\theta)$ such that $\sigma_\alpha\phi = \phi_\alpha$, for all $\alpha \in A$. It follows that

(7) $$x_1\sigma_{\alpha_1} < x_2\sigma_{\alpha_2} \quad (\text{in } X),$$

for all $x_1 \in X_{\alpha_1}$ and all $x_2 \in X_{\alpha_2}$. But in the same way one can show that $x_1\sigma_{\alpha_1} > x_2\sigma_{\alpha_2}$, for all $x_1 \in X_{\alpha_1}$ and $x_2 \in X_{\alpha_2}$, which is contradictory.

Although proposition 2.7.1 suggests the opposite, it is true that $K(LO,\theta)$ always contains universal morphisms and bimorphisms (provided that the Generalized Continuum Hypothesis holds). In order to prove this we need several lemmas. We refer to section 1.5 for the notation used.

2.7.3. LEMMA. Let $\theta, \kappa \in$ ORD, and suppose $K(LO)$ admits a $K(LO,\theta)$-universal object of cardinality $\aleph_\kappa$. Then $K(LO,\kappa)$ contains a bimorphism $\tau : B \to B$ with the following property: for every bimorphism $\phi : X \to X$ in $K(LO,\theta)$ and for every $x \in X$ there exists a 1-1 order-preserving map $\mu : \Delta_\phi(x) \to B$ such that $\mu\circ\tau = (\phi \mid \Delta_\phi(x))\circ\mu$.

PROOF. Let $E = \{-1,0,1\}$, ordered as usual, and let A be a $K(LO,\theta)$-universal object in $K(LO)$ with $\mathrm{card}(A) = \aleph_\kappa$. We put $B = E \times I \times A$, ordered lexicographically, and we define $\tau : B \to B$ by

(8) $$(e,n,a)\tau = (e,n-e,a)$$

for arbitrary $(e,n,a) \in B$. Clearly τ is a bimorphism of $K(LO,\kappa)$.

Let $\phi: X \to X$ be an arbitrary bimorphism of $K(LO,\theta)$, and let $x \in X$. If $x = x\phi$, then $\Delta_\phi(x) = \{x\}$, and for $x\mu$ we may take any point $(0,n,a) \in B$. Suppose $x \neq x_\phi$; then $\Delta_\phi(x)$ is infinite.

As A is $K(LO,\theta)$-universal, there exists a 1-1 order-preserving map $\sigma: S \to A$, where S is the interval $[x;x\phi)$ if $x < x\phi$, and $S=(x\phi;x]$ if $x > x\phi$. Let $y \in \Delta_\phi(x)$. There is a unique $k \in I$ such that $y\phi^k \in S$ (proposition 1.5.13); we define

$$y\mu = (e, e.k, y\phi^k\sigma), \tag{9}$$

where $e=-1$ if $x \in X_{\phi,+}$ and $e=+1$ if $x \in X_{\phi,-}$.

The map $\mu : \Delta_\phi(x) \to B$ is 1-1 and order-preserving. For let $y_1, y_2 \in \Delta_\phi(x)$, $y_1 < y_2$. Say $x < x\phi$. There are $k_1, k_2 \in I$ such that $y_i\phi^{k_i} \in S$ $(i=1,2)$. If $k_1 = k_2$ we have $y_1\phi^{k_1} < y_2\phi^{k_2}$ and hence $y_1\mu < y_2\mu$. If $k_1 \neq k_2$ we must have $k_1 > k_2$ (as $k_1 < k_2 \Rightarrow y_1\phi^{k_1} < y_2\phi^{k_1} < y_2\phi^{k_2} \in S \Rightarrow y_1\phi^{k_1} \notin S$); hence $e.k_1 < e.k_2$, and again $y_1\mu < y_2\mu$.

Finally, $\mu \circ \tau = (\phi | \Delta_\phi(x)) \circ \mu$. For let $y \in \Delta_\phi(x)$, and let $k \in I$ such that $y\phi^k \in S$; then

$$y\mu\circ\tau = (e, e.k, y\phi^k\sigma)\tau = (e, e.(k-1), (y\phi)\phi^{k-1}\sigma) = y\phi\mu. \tag{10}$$

2.7.4. LEMMA. Let $\theta, \kappa \in ORD$, and suppose $K(LO)$ admits a $K(LO,\theta)$-universal object of power $\aleph_\kappa$. Then $K(LO,\kappa)$ contains a morphism $\tau_0 : B_0 \to B_0$ with the following property: for every morphism $\phi : X \to X$ in $K(LO,\theta)$ with a fixed point a there exists a 1-1 order-preserving map $\mu : \Delta_\phi(a) \to B_0$ such that $\mu\circ\tau_0 = (\phi | \Delta_\phi(a))\circ\mu$.

PROOF. Let A be a $K(LO,\theta)$-universal object with $card(A) = \aleph_\kappa$. Let $A_0 = \{0\}$ and, for $n \in N$, $A_{n+1} = A_\infty \times A_n$, ordered lexicographically; then $A_n \cap A_m = \emptyset$ if $n \neq m$. Let $C = \bigcup_{n=0}^{\infty} A_n$; if $c \in C$, the $n \in N$ such that $c \in A_n$ will be denoted by n_c. It is immediate that C is linearly ordered by the following relation :

$$c_1 \leq c_2 \Longleftrightarrow (n_{c_1} > n_{c_2}) \vee ((n_{c_1} = n_{c_2} = n) \wedge (c_1 \leq c_2 \text{ in } A_n)). \tag{11}$$

Let $\sigma_0 = i_{A_0}$, and let $\sigma_{n+1} : A_{n+1} \to A_n$, $n \in N$, be defined by

(12) $$(a',a)\sigma_n = a' \quad (a' \in A_n, a \in A).$$

Let $\sigma : C \to C$ be the "union" of the maps $\sigma_n : \sigma \mid A_n = \sigma_n$, for each $n \in N$. The map σ is an increasing translation.

Let D be a set such that $D \cap C = \{0\}$, $\mathrm{card}(D) = \mathrm{card}(C)$ $(= \aleph_\kappa)$, and let f be a 1-1 map of $C \setminus \{0\}$ onto $D \setminus \{0\}$. We order D by defining, for arbitrary $d_1, d_2 \in D$:

(13) $$d_1 \leqq d_2 \Longleftrightarrow d_2 f^{-1} \leqq d_1 f^{-1} \quad \text{in } C;$$

let $B_o = C \cup D$, ordered in such a way that C and D retain their ordering while furthermore every $c \in C$ preceeds every $d \in D$. The map $\tau_o : B_o \to B_o$ is defined in the following manner:

(14) $$\tau_o \mid C = \sigma;$$
$$\tau_o \mid (D \setminus \{0\}) = f^{-1} \circ \sigma \circ f.$$

Then $\mathrm{card}(B_o) = \aleph_\kappa$; we will show that τ_o has the required property.

Let $\phi : X \to X$ be a morphism of $K(LO,\theta)$ with a fixed point a. Then $\Delta_\phi(a) = TO_\phi(a)$ (proposition 1.5.10). We will first define a 1-1 order-preserving map $\nu : \Delta_\phi(a) \cap X_{\phi,+} \to C$ such that

(15) $$\nu \circ \tau_o = (\phi \mid (\Delta_\phi(a) \cap X_{\phi,+})) \circ \nu .$$

Let $E_{-1} = E_o = \{a\}$, $E_1 = a\phi^{-1} \setminus X_{\phi,-}$, $E_{n+1} = E_n \phi^{-1}$ $(n \in N)$. The sets E_n, $n \in N$, are disjoint and cover $\Delta_\phi(a) \cap X_{\phi,+}$. We define ν in such a way that $E_n \nu \subset A_n$. Then necessarily $a\nu = 0$. Suppose for all $k \leqq n$, $n \in N$, the map $\nu | E_k$ is already defined in such a way that

(i) $\nu | E_k$ is a 1-1 order-preserving map $E_k \to A_k$;

(ii) $(\nu|E_k) \circ \sigma_k = (\phi|E_k) \circ (\nu|E_{k-1})$.

Then it is possible to define $\nu | E_{n+1}$ such that (i) and (ii) are also satisfied for k=n+1. For lèt x_o be an arbitrary point of E_n; as $\mathrm{card}(x_o\phi^{-1}) \leqq \aleph_\theta$, there exists a 1-1 order-preserving map $\omega_{x_o} : x_o\phi^{-1} \to A$. If now x is an arbitrary point of E_{n+1}, we put

(16) $$x\nu = (x\phi\nu, x\omega_{x\phi}) \in A_{n+1}.$$

In this way we arrive at a 1-1 order-preserving map ν, $\nu : (\Delta_\phi(a) \cap X_{\phi,+}) \to C$, satisfying (15).

In the same way there exists a 1-1 order-preserving map $\rho : (\Delta_\phi(a) \cap X_{\phi,-}) \to D$ such that

(17) $$\rho \circ \tau_0 = (\phi | (\Delta_\phi(a) \cap X_{\phi,-})) \circ \rho ,$$

and such that $a\rho = 0 = a\nu$. If we define $\mu : \Delta_\phi(a) \to B_0$ through

(18) $$\mu | (\Delta_\phi(a) \cap X_{\phi,+}) = \nu , \qquad \mu | (\Delta_\phi(a) \cap X_{\phi,-}) = \rho ,$$

then μ is a 1-1 and order-preserving map, while $\mu \circ \tau_0 = (\phi | \Delta_\phi(a)) \circ \mu$.

2.7.5. LEMMA. Let $\theta, \kappa \in$ ORD, and suppose K(LO) admits a K(LO,θ)-universal object of cardinality $\aleph_\kappa$. Then K(LO,κ) contains a morphism $\tau_1 : B_1 \to B_1$ with the following property: if $\phi : X \to X$ is a morphism of K_0, and if $x \in X_{\phi,+}$ such that $TO_\phi(x)$ contains no fixed point, then there exists a 1-1 order-preserving map $\mu : TO_\phi(x) \to B_1$ such that $\mu \circ \tau_1 = (\phi | TO_\phi(x)) \circ \mu$.

PROOF. Let A be a K(LO,θ)-universal object with card(A) $= \aleph_\kappa$, and let $A' = A \times \{1,2\} \cup \{0\}$, ordered as follows:

(19) $$(a_1, 1) < 0 < (a_2, 2)$$

for arbitrary $a_1, a_2 \in A$;

(20) $$(a_1, i) \leq (a_2, i) \Longleftrightarrow a_1 \leq a_2$$

if $a_1, a_2 \in A$ and $i \in \{1,2\}$. Then A' is a K(LO,θ)-universal object of power $\aleph_\kappa$ with the following additional property: if Y is any object of K(LO,θ) and y an arbitrary point of Y, there exists a monomorphism $\mu' : Y \to A'$ with $y\mu' = 0$.

For each $k \in I$, let $M_k = \{h \in I : h \geq k\}$, and let $C_k = (A')^{M_k}$. Let $C = \bigcup_{k \in I} C_k$; if $c \in C$, we write k_c for the uniquely determined $k \in I$ such that $c \in C_k$. Furthermore, let $\sigma : C \to C$ be the following map: if

$c \in C$, then

(21) $$c\sigma = c|M_{k_c+1} \, .$$

Let c_o be the element of C_o mapping every $k \in M_o$ onto $0 \in A'$; let $B_1 = TO_\sigma(c_o)$ and $\tau_1 = \sigma|B_1$. Then $\mathrm{card}(B_1) = \aleph_\kappa$ (cf. the construction in the proof of lemma 2.6.3).

If $c \in C$, we have

(22) $$c \in B_1 \Longleftrightarrow (\exists k \geq k_c)((M_k)c = \{0\}).$$

Hence if $c_1, c_2 \in B_1$, the following integer is well-defined:

(23) $$k_{c_1,c_2} = \text{the smallest } k \in I \text{ such that } k \geq k_{c_1},\ k \geq k_{c_2}$$
$$\text{and } c_1|M_{k+1} = c_2|M_{k+1}.$$

Clearly B_1 is linearly ordered by the following binary relation $\leq$:

(24) $$c_1 \leq c_2 \Longleftrightarrow (k_{c_1} < k_{c_2}) \vee ((k_{c_1} = k_{c_2}) \wedge ((k_{c_1,c_2})c_1 \leq (k_{c_1,c_2})c_2$$
$$\text{(in } A'))).$$

It is easily verified that in this ordering the map τ_1 is an increasing translation.

Now let $\phi : X \to X$ be an arbitrary morphism of $K(LO,\theta)$, and let $x \in X_{\phi,+}$ such that $TO_\phi(x)$ contains no fixed point. We must define a 1-1 order-preserving map $\mu : TO_\phi(x) \to B_1$, such that

(25) $$\mu \circ \tau_1 = (\phi|TO_\phi(x)) \circ \mu \, .$$

Let $X_o = O_\phi(x)$, $X_1 = X_o\phi^{-1} \setminus X_o$, $X_{n+1} = X_n\phi^{-1}$ $(n \geq 1)$. We first define $\mu|(X_o \cup X_1)$.

If $n \in N$, let

(26) $$Y_n = \{c \in B_1 : c\tau_1 = c_o\tau_1{}^n\} \, .$$

As $c \in Y_n \Longleftrightarrow (k_c = n-1) \wedge (c|M_n = c_o|M_n)$, the map $c \to (n-1)c$ is an order-isomorphism of Y_n onto A'. Consequently for every $n \in N$ there exists a 1-1 order-preserving map $\nu_n : (x\phi^n)\phi^{-1} \to Y_n$ which maps (in case $n \geq 1$) the point $x\phi^{n-1}$ onto $c_o\tau_1^{n-1}$. We put

(27) $$\mu|(x\phi^n)\phi^{-1} = \nu_n$$

for each $n \in N$. Thus μ is defined on all of $X_o \cup X_1$. And μ is 1-1 and order-preserving on $X_o \cup X_1$; for let $x_1, x_2 \in X_o \cup X_1$, $x_1 < x_2$. Then take $n_1, n_2 \in N$ such that $x_i\phi = x\phi^{n_i}$ $(i=1,2)$. If $n_1 < n_2$, then $k_{x_1\mu} < k_{x_2\mu}$ and hence $x_1\mu < x_2\mu$. If $n_1=n_2=n$, then

(28) $$x_1\mu = x_1\nu_n < x_2\nu_n = x_2\mu .$$

Moreover, one verifies at once that

(29) $$(\mu\,|(X_o \cup X_1)) \circ \tau_1 = (\phi\,|(X_o \cup X_1)) \circ (\mu|(X_o \cup X_1)).$$

Assume now μ to be defined already on $\bigcup_{k=0}^{n} X_k$ $(n \geq 1)$ in such a way that it is a 1-1 order-preserving map satisfying

(30) $$z\mu\tau_1 = z\phi\mu$$

for all $z \in \bigcup_{k=0}^{n} X_k$. Let $z \in X_n$; as $\mathrm{card}(z\phi^{-1}) \leq \aleph_\theta$, and as $(z\mu)\tau_1^{-1}$ is order-isomorphic to A', there exists a 1-1 order-preserving map $\pi_z : z\phi^{-1} \to (z\mu)\tau_1^{-1}$. We put

(31) $$\mu|z\phi^{-1} = \pi_z$$

and obtain in this way (letting z run through X_n) a 1-1 order-preserving map on $\bigcup_{k=0}^{n+1} X_k$, satisfying (30) on that set. Using induction the existence of a monomorphism $\mu : TO_\phi(x) \to B_1$ satisfying (25) follows.

2.7.6. LEMMA. Let θ, $\kappa \in$ ORD, and suppose K(LO) admits a K(LO,θ)-universal object of power $\aleph_\kappa$. Then K(LO,κ) contains a morphism $\tau_2 : B_2 \to B_2$ with the following property: if $\phi : X \to X$ is any morphism of K(LO,θ), and if $x \in X_{\phi,+}$ such that $\Delta_\phi(x)$ contains no fixed points, then there exists a 1-1 order-preserving map $\mu : \Delta_\phi(x) \to B_2$ such that $\mu \circ \tau_2 = (\phi|\Delta_\phi(x)) \circ \mu$.

PROOF. Let A be a K(LO,θ)-universal object with $\mathrm{card}(A) = \aleph_\theta$, and let

$\tau_1 : B_1 \to B_1$ be the map defined in the proof of the previous lemma. Let B_2 be the set $B_1 \times A$, linearly ordered as follows: if $(b_i, a_i) \in B_2$ $(i=1,2)$, then

(32) $$(b_1,a_1) \leq (b_2,a_2) \Longleftrightarrow (k_{b_1} < k_{b_2}) \vee ((k_{b_1} = k_{b_2}) \wedge (a_1 < a_2)) \vee \vee ((k_{b_1} = k_{b_2}) \wedge (a_1 = a_2) \wedge (b_1 \leq b_2)).$$

We define $\tau_2 : B_2 \to B_2$ by

(33) $$(b,a)\tau_2 = (b\tau_1, a).$$

Then τ_2 is a right translation of B_2.

Let $\phi \in K(LO,\theta)$, $\phi : X \to X$, and let $x \in X$ such that $\Delta_\phi(x)$ contains no fixed point and $x < x\phi$. As the set $\Lambda_\phi(x)$, ordered by $\leq_{\phi,x}$, is an object of $K(LO,\theta)$, there exists a 1-1 order-preserving map $\lambda : \Lambda_\phi(x) \to A$. In the remainder of this proof we will just write Λ and $\leq$ for $\Lambda_\phi(x)$ and $\leq_{\phi,x}$ respectively.

For every $L \in \Lambda$ we choose an $n_L \in N$ and an $x_L \in L$ such that

(34) $$x\phi^{n_L} \leq x_L < x\phi^{n_L+1};$$

in case $L = TO_\phi(x)$ we take care to choose $n_L = 0$ and $x_L = x$. By lemma 2.7.5 there exists for each $L \in \Lambda$ a 1-1 order-preserving map $\mu_L : L \to B$, such that

(35) $$\mu_L \circ \tau_1 = (\phi | L) \circ \mu_L$$

and

(36) $$(x_L)\mu_L = (c_o)\tau_1^{n_L}$$

(c_o stands for the same entity as in the previous proof).

We define $\mu : \Delta_\phi(x) \to B_2$ as follows: if $z \in \Delta_\phi(x)$, and if $L = TO_\phi(z)$, then

(37) $$z\mu = (z\mu_L, L\lambda).$$

We will show that μ meets the requirements set forth in the lemma.

First we show that

(38) $$\mu \circ \tau_2 = (\phi | \Delta_\phi(x)) \circ \mu .$$

Let $z \in \Delta_\phi(x)$, and let $L = TO_\phi(z)$. Then

(39)
$$z\mu\tau_2 = (z\mu_L, L\lambda)\tau_2 = (z\mu_L\tau_1, L\lambda) = = (z\phi\mu_L, L\lambda) = z\phi\mu ,$$

as $TO_\phi(z\phi) = L$.

Next we show that μ is 1-1 and order-preserving. Let $z_1, z_2 \in \Delta_\phi(x)$, $z_1 < z_2$. Put $TO_\phi(z_i) = L_i$ $(i=1,2)$. If $L_1 = L_2 = L$, then $z_1\mu_L < z_2\mu_L$; it follows that either $k_{z_1\mu_L} < k_{z_2\mu_L}$ - implying $z_1\mu_L < z_2\mu_L$ - or $k_{z_1\mu_L} = k_{z_2\mu_L}$, in which case it follows that $z_1\mu < z_2\mu$ by the third clause of (32).

Suppose now that $L_1 \neq L_2$. In order to simplify the notation, we will write μ_i instead of μ_{L_i}, k_i instead of $k_{z_i\mu_i}$, x_i instead of x_{L_i} and n_i instead of n_{L_i} $(i=1,2)$.

If $k_1 < k_2$, obviously $z_1\mu < z_2\mu$; suppose therefore that $k_1 = k_2 = k$. We will show that $L_1 < L_2$; it then follows (second clause of (32)) that $z_1\mu < z_2\mu$, and the proof will be finished.

Let $n \geqq k_{z_i\mu_i, x_i\mu_i}$, $i=1,2$ (cf. (23)). Then $n \geqq k, n_1, n_2$. Moreover,

(40)
$$z_i\phi^{n-k}\mu_i = z_i\mu_i\tau_1^{n-k} = x_i\mu_i\tau^{n-n_i} = x_i\phi^{n-n_i}\mu_i$$

(using (35), (36) and (23)); as μ_i is 1-1, it follows that

(41)
$$z_i\phi^{n-k} = x_i\phi^{n-n_i} \quad (i=1,2).$$

From (34) and the fact that $z_1 < z_2$ and $L_1 \neq L_2$ we conclude that

(42)
$$x\phi^n \leqq z_1\phi^{n-k} < z_2\phi^{n-k} \leqq x\phi^{n+1} .$$

If $z_2\phi^{n-k} < x\phi^{k+1}$, it follows from the definition of the order $\leqq_{x,\phi}$ in Λ that $L_1 < L_2$. We will conclude the proof by showing that the assumption $z_2\phi^{n-k} = x\phi^{n+1}$ leads to a contradiction.

If $z_2\phi^{n-k} = x\phi^{n+1}$, then $L_2 = TO_\phi(x)$, hence $n_2 = 0$ and $x_2 = x$. It follows that

(43)
$$x\phi^n = x_2\phi^{n-n_2} = z_2\phi^{n-k} = x\phi^{k+1} ,$$

by (41) and the assumption; hence $\Delta_\phi(x)$ contains a fixed point, contrary to our hypotheses.

2.7.7. LEMMA. Let $\theta, \kappa \in$ ORD, and suppose K(LO) admits a K(LO,θ)-universal object A with card(A) $= \aleph_\kappa$. Then K(LO,κ) contains a morphism $\tau : B \to B$ with the following property: if $\phi : X \to X$ is any morphism of K(LO,θ), and if $x \in X$, there exists a 1-1 order-preserving map $\mu : \Delta_\phi(x) \to B$ such that $\mu \circ \tau_3 = (\phi | \Delta_\phi(x)) \circ \mu$.

PROOF. It follows from lemma 2.7.6 (reversing orderings) that there exists a morphism $\tau_3 : B_3 \to B_3$ in K(LO,κ) with the property: if $\phi : X \to X$ is a morphism of K(LO,θ), $x \in X_{\phi,-}$, and if $\Delta_\phi(x)$ contains no fixed point under ϕ, then there exists a 1-1 order-preserving map $\mu : \Delta_\phi(x) \to B_3$ such that $\mu \circ \tau_3 = (\phi | \Delta_\phi(x)) \circ \mu$.

Let $\tau_o : B_o \to B_o$ and $\tau_2 : B_2 \to B_2$ be morphisms of K(LO,κ) satisfying the requirements of lemma 2.7.4 and lemma 2.7.6, respectively. Let B be the set of all ordered pairs (n,b) with $n \in \{0,2,3\}$ and $b \in B_n$, ordered as follows:

(44) $$(0,b_o) < (2,b_2) < (3,b_3)$$

for arbitrary $b_o \in B_o$, $b_2 \in B_2$ and $b_3 \in B_3$;

(45) $$(n,b_1) \leqq (n,b_2) \Longleftrightarrow b_1 \leqq b_2 \quad (\text{in } B_n)$$

for $n \in \{0,2,3\}$. Then, as card(B) $= \aleph_\kappa$, B is an object of K(PO,κ). Furthermore, let $\tau : B \to B$ be defined in the following manner:

(46) $$\begin{aligned}(0,b)\tau &= (0,b\tau_o) \text{ for all } b \in B_o;\\ (2,b)\tau &= (2,b\tau_2) \text{ for all } b \in B_2;\\ (3,b)\tau &= (3,b\tau_3) \text{ for all } b \in B_3.\end{aligned}$$

Then τ is order-preserving, and it follows from the lemmas 2.7.4 and 2.7.6 and our remarks above that τ has the properties required.

2.7.8. THEOREM. K(LO) contains K(LO,θ)-universal morphisms and bimorphisms, for every $\theta \in$ ORD. More exactly, if A is a K(LO,θ)-universal object of K(LO), and if $\aleph_\kappa$ = card(A), then already K(LO,κ)

contains K(LO, θ)-universal morphisms and bimorphisms.

PROOF. First we show that K(LO, θ)-universal bimorphisms exist. Let $\tau : B \to B$ be a bimorphism of K(LO, κ) meeting the requirements of lemma 2.7.3, and let $C = A \times B$, ordered lexicographically. We define $\Phi : C \to C$ by

$$(47) \qquad (a,b)\Phi = (a,b\tau) \quad ((a,b) \in C).$$

It is immediate that Φ is a bimorphism of K(LO, κ).

Let $\phi: X \to X$ be an arbitrary bimorphism of K(LO, θ). The set X/Δ_ϕ is a linearly ordered set of cardinality at most $\aleph_\theta$; hence there exists a 1-1 order-preserving map $\delta : X/\Delta_\phi \to A$. For every $D \in X/\Delta_\phi$, let μ_D be a 1-1 order-preserving map $D \to B$ such that $\mu_D \circ \tau = (\phi|D) \circ \mu_D$ (the existence of these μ_D is guaranteed by lemma 2.7.3).

We now define $\mu : X \to C$. If $x \in X$, we put

$$(48) \qquad x\mu = ((\Delta_\phi(x))\delta,\ x\mu_{\Delta_\phi(x)}).$$

Then μ is a monomorphism. For let $x_1, x_2 \in X$, $x_1 < x_2$. If $\Delta_\phi(x_1) < \Delta_\phi(x_2)$ in X/Δ_ϕ, then $(\Delta_\phi(x_1))\delta < (\Delta_\phi(x_2))\delta$ and hence $x_1\mu < x_2\mu$. If $x_1 \Delta_\phi x_2$, then

$$(49) \qquad x_1\mu_{\Delta\phi(x_1)} < x_2\mu_{\Delta_\phi(x_1)} = x_2\mu_{\Delta_\phi(x_2)}$$

and again $x_1\mu < x_2\mu$.

Finally $\mu\Phi = \phi\mu$. For let $x \in X$; then

$$(50) \qquad \begin{aligned} x\mu\Phi &= ((\Delta_\phi(x))\delta, x\mu_{\Delta_\phi(x)})\Phi = ((\Delta_\phi(x))\delta, x\mu_{\Delta_\phi(x)}\tau) = \\ &= ((\Delta_\phi(x))\delta,\ (x\phi)\mu_{\Delta_\phi(x)}) = x\phi\mu, \end{aligned}$$

as $\Delta_\phi(x) = \Delta_\phi(x\phi)$.

The proof of the existence of a K(LO, θ)-universal morphism in K(LO, κ) is almost verbally the same, now using, however, lemma 2.7.7 instead of lemma 2.7.3.

2.7.9. COROLLARY. Let $\theta \in$ ORD. If K(LO, θ) admits a universal object, it contains universal morphisms and bimorphisms.

*2.7.10. COROLLARY. K(LO, θ) contains universal morphisms and bimorphisms, for every $\theta \in$ ORD.

2.7.11. COROLLARY. K(LO,0) contains a universal bimorphism $\Phi: Q \to Q$ and a universal morphism $\Psi : Q \to Q$ (Q denoting the set of rational numbers with its usual ordering).

PROOF. Let $\Phi_o : C \to C$ be a universal bimorphism in K(LO,0); as Q is a universal object in K (proposition 1.4.4), such a Φ_o exists. Then $C \times Q$, ordered lexicographically, has the same order type as Q (see e.g. [56] Ch.4 § 7), and $\Phi_1 : C \times Q \to C \times Q$, defined by

(51) $$(c,q)\,\Phi_1 = (c\Phi_o, q)$$

is again a universal bimorphism. From this the existence of Φ follows. The existence of Ψ is proved in a similar manner.

2.8. Notes

A very simple idea lies at the origin of the main constructions of this chapter, namely, the idea of the graph of a map.

For example, let f be a continuous map of a topological space X_1 into a space X_2. Then, as is well-known, the graph Γ of f, considered as a subspace of the topological product $X_1 \times X_2$, is topologically equivalent to X_1, and the map τ,

(1) $$x\,\tau = (x, xf)$$

is a homeomorphism of X_1 onto Γ.

If we denote by π_2 the canonical projection $X_1 \times X_2 \to X_2$,

(2) $$(x_1, x_2)\,\pi_2 = x_2,$$

then f is equivalent to the restricted map $\pi_2|\Gamma$, up to the topological deformation τ, as $\tau \circ \pi_2 = f$.

If f_1 is another continuous map $X_1 \to X_2$, with graph Γ_1, then f_1 is equivalent to a restriction $\pi_2 | \Gamma_1$ of the same continuous map π_2, now up to a new topological embedding $\tau_1 : X_1 \to X_1 \times X_2$,

(3) $$x\tau_1 = (x, xf_1)$$

Thus in a certain sense π_2 is "universal" for all continuous maps of X_1 into X_2.

Similarly, if X_1 and X_2 are groups and if $f : X_1 \to X_2$ is a homomorphism, then the graph Γ of f is a subgroup of the direct product $X_1 \times X_2$, the map τ, defined by (1), is an isomorphism of X_1 onto Γ, and π_2 is a homomorphic map of $X_1 \times X_2$ into X_2 which is somehow "universal" for all homomorphisms $X_1 \to X_2$.

This use of the graph is well-known. It has, however, a serious draw-back, especially if the original maps f, f_1, are self-maps $X \to X$. In this case it is annoying that the new map $\pi_2 | \Gamma$ is no longer a self-map: it sends one copy of X (namely Γ) into a different copy of X (namely X itself). The root of the difficulty lies in the fact that no natural equivalence between $X \times X$ and X exists.

In 1959 J. DE GROOT ([47,48]; see also A.H. COPELAND JR. and J. DE GROOT [17,18]) and G.-C. ROTA ([90] ; see also [91,92]) independently made use of the same device to remedy this. In a final analysis one could say that their method is based on the fact that $1 + \aleph_0 = \aleph_0$.

In fact, let $f : X \to X$ be a self-map. Instead of the map τ of X onto the graph of f in $X \times X$, as defined by (1), we consider the map σ of X into X^N, defined as follows:

(4) $$x\sigma = (x, xf, xf^2, \ldots, xf^n, \ldots).$$

The projection map π_2 of (2) amounts to a striking out of the first coordinate; we replace it by a map $\mu : X^N \to X^N$ which formally does the same:

(5) $$(x_1, x_2, x_3, \ldots, x_n, \ldots)\mu = (x_2, x_3, \ldots, x_{n+1}, \ldots).$$

One verifies at once that

(6) $$\mu | X\tau = \sigma^{-1} \circ f \circ \sigma.$$

If e.g. X is a topological space and f is continuous, then σ is a topological embedding of X into X^N, and the map $\mu : X^N \to X^N$ is in its turn continuous. Hence μ is universal for all continuous maps $X \to X$, in the sense that μ contains copies of all these maps. More exactly, if $f : X \to X$ is an arbitrary continuous map, then X^N contains a topological copy of X on which μ behaves exactly in the same way as f does on X.

The map μ defined by (4) is induced by the successor map $\phi : N \to N$ (ϕ sends n into n+1, for all $n \in N$), in the sense that

(7) $$(x_1, x_2, x_3, \ldots, x_n, \ldots)\mu = (x_{1\phi}, x_{2\phi}, x_{3\phi}, \ldots, x_{n\phi}, \ldots).$$

Now let G be a semigroup. If $\gamma_o \in G$, the left translation $\overline{\gamma_o} : G \to G$ induces in the same way a map $\mu : X^G \to X^G$: if $x = (x_\gamma)_{\gamma \in G} \in X^G$, then $x\mu = y = (y_\gamma)_{\gamma \in G}$, where $y_\gamma = x_{\gamma_o \gamma}$. Considerations of this kind led J. DE GROOT [47] to a proof of the existence of universal bimorphisms and universal groups of bimorphisms in $K^\theta(CR)$ (theorem 2.5.13 and half of theorem 2.5.21); see also J. DE GROOT [49] .

An analysis of these considerations lead to the concept of a star functor, and to a new formulation, in terms of category theory. Some partial results in this direction have been mentioned in [8] ; a further analysis along the same lines resulted in the sections 2.2, 2.3 and 2.4 of this chapter.

We mentioned already that theorem 2.5.13 and the part of theorem 2.5.21 concerning $K^\theta(CR)$ are due to J. DE GROOT ([47,49]). Theorem 2.5.9 follows (in the case θ=0) from a stronger result of A.H. COPELAND JR and J. DE GROOT ([17,18] ; see corollary 4.5.3 and proposition 4.5.6 below). The case θ=0 of theorem 2.5.19 is an immediate consequence of an unpublished result of J. DE GROOT (corollary 4.5.2 and proposition 4.5.5 below). Theorem 2.5.11 is due to P.C. BAAYEN and J. DE GROOT (see [6] and [8]), to whom its assertion was raised as a problem by R.D. ANDERSON. The results of 2.6 were obtained by P.C. BAAYEN and J. DE GROOT in collaboration; they have been published already in the form of a preliminary note [9] . The results of section 2.7 are taken from another preliminary note, P.C. BAAYEN [7] .

3. UNIVERSAL CONTINUOUS MAPS

3.1. Categories of topological spaces

In section 1.2 it was remarked that in categories of topological spaces epimorphisms need not always be mappings onto; likewise monomorphisms are not always topological embedding maps. For this reason the results of section 2.5 are not fully satisfactory as far as they concern topological spaces. In fact, the very concepts of universal and dually universal morphisms and systems of morphisms as defined in chapter 2 are not adequate for categories of topological spaces.

It turns out that the constructions of chapter 2 lead, in the case of categories of topological spaces, to results stronger than expressed in that chapter.

In this section we define the concepts obtained by adapting the definitions of section 2.1 to the situation occurring when continuous maps are considered.

3.1.1. DEFINITION. Let K be a category of topological spaces, i.e. a concrete category, the objects of which are provided with topologies, while its morphisms are continuous maps with respect to these topologies. Let K_o be a subcategory of K. A <u>topologically K_o-universal object</u> of K is an object A of K with the property that for every object B of K_o there exists a <u>topological</u> map $\mu \in K$, $\mu : B \to A$. A <u>topologically dually K_o-universal object of K</u> is an object A of K with the property that for every object B of K_o there exists a continuous map $\nu \in K$ of A <u>onto</u> B.

It is easily verified that the universal and dually universal objects of categories of topological spaces, mentioned in section 1.4, are all topologically (dually) universal: C is a topologically universal object for $K^o(CZ)$ and $K^o(ZM)$, and a topologically dually universal object for $K^o(CZ)$; if the Generalized Continuum Hypothesis is valid, a topologically dually universal object exists for each $K^\theta(CZ)$, $\theta \in ORD$; $\{0,1\}^{\aleph_\theta}$ and $[0,1]^{\aleph_\theta}$ are topologically universal objects for $K^\theta(CZ)$ and $K^\theta(CR)$, respectively ($\theta \in ORD$); each Hilbert space of weight $\aleph_\theta$ is both a topologically universal and a topologically dually universal object for $K^\theta(H)$, $\theta \in ORD$, and is also a topologically universal object for $K^\theta(M)$; $T^{\aleph_o}$ is a topologically universal object for K(CMAG), and the groups M,S and D of section 1.4 are topologically dually universal objects for K(CMoG), K(CS) and K(ZCMoG), respectively.

3.1.2. DEFINITION. Let K be a category of topological spaces, and let K_o be a subcategory of K. A topologically K_o-universal morphism in K is a morphism $\phi : A \to A$ in K with the following property: for every morphism ψ of K_o of which the source and sink coincide, $\psi : B \to B$, there exists a topological map $\mu \in K$, $\mu : B \to A$, such that $\mu\phi = \psi\mu$. A topologically dually K_o-universal morphism in K is a morphism $\phi : A \to A$ in K enjoying the following property: for every morphism ψ of K_o of which the source and sink coincide, $\psi : B \to B$, there exists a continuous map $\nu \in K$, mapping A onto B in such a way that $\phi\nu = \nu\psi$.

Topologically K_o-universal bimorphisms and topologically dually K_o-universal bimorphisms are defined similarly, and also topologically (dually) (K_o, κ)-universal semigroups of morphisms or groups of bimorphisms.

The results of section 2.1 remain valid for the corresponding topological concepts.

If all objects of K are compact topological spaces, then all continuous 1-1 maps belonging to K are topological, and all $\nu \in K$ with a dense image are onto. Consequently in the categories K(CZ), K(CMAG) and K(CMoG) and their subcategories every (dually) universal object (morphism, bimorphism, system of morphisms) is always topologically (dually) universal. The same holds for the categories $K^\theta(H)$ (cf. propositions 1.2.5 and 1.2.8). In the next sections we will exhibit other arguments for this, which remain valid for categories like $K^o(M)$, $K^o(ZM)$ or $K^\theta(CR)$.

3.2. Neat categories

The existence of universal morphisms or systems of morphisms was proved in section 2.4 for categories in which - among other conditions - suitable direct joins exist. When categories of topological spaces are considered, the natural candidates for direct joins are the topological products, with their natural projection maps.

We will show in this section that in the categories which interest us, direct joins, if they exist, are indeed equivalent to topological products; in most (but not all) of them free joins, if they exist, turn out to be topological sums.

3.2.1. DEFINITION. We will say that a category K of topological spaces is neat if in it the following condition is satisfied: whenever a family $(X_t)_{t \in T}$ of objects of K admits a direct join in K, the topological product $X = \mathbb{P}_{t \in T} X_t$ is also an object of K, all canonical projections $\pi_t : X_t \to X_t$, $t \in T$, are morphisms of K, and $X = \prod_{t \in T} X_t(\pi_t)$ in K.

The category K is called co-neat if it satisfies the "dual" condition: whenever a family $(X_t)_{t \in T}$ of objects of K admits a free join in K, then a topological sum $X = \sum_{t \in T} X_t$ is also an object of K, all canonical injections $\sigma_t : X_t \to X$ $(t \in T)$ belong to K, and $X = \mathop{\ast}_{t \in T} (\sigma_t)$ in K.

REMARK 1. It should be emphasized that neatness and co-neatness are concepts that do not belong to category theory proper; in particular, the property of being co-neat is not dual to the property of being neat.

The following two lemma's are evident:

3.2.2. LEMMA. Let K be a full subcategory of the category of all Hausdorff topological spaces. Then if the topological product $X = \mathbb{P}_{t \in T} X_t$ of a family of objects $(X_t)_{t \in T}$ of K is itself an object of K, it is also a direct join of $(X_t)_{t \in T}$ in K, $X = \prod_{t \in T} X_t\ (\pi_t)$.

3.2.3. LEMMA. Let K be a full subcategory of the category of all Hausdorff topological spaces. If a topological sum $X = \sum_{t \in T} X_t$ of a family of objects $(X_t)_{t \in T}$ of K is itself an object of K, then it is also a free join, $X = \mathop{\ast}_{t \in T} X_t\ (\sigma_t)$.

3.2.4. PROPOSITION. $K^{\theta}(CZ)$ is neat, for each $\theta \in ORD$.

PROOF. Suppose $X = \prod_{t \in T} X_t\ (\rho_t)$; let X^* designate the topological product

$$X^* = \mathbb{P}_{t \in T} X_t \tag{1}$$

and let π_t be the canonical projection $X^* \to X_t$, for each $t \in T$.

We define a map $\mu: X \to X^*$ as follows: if $x \in X$, then

$$x\mu = (x\rho_t)_{t \in T} \in X^* . \tag{2}$$

As $\mu\circ\pi_t = \rho_t$, for all $t \in T$, and as all ρ_t are continuous, μ is a continuous map. We will show that μ is a topological map of X onto X^*.

First we show that μ is 1-1. Suppose this were not the case. Then $x\mu = y\mu$ for some $x,y \in X$, $x \neq y$. It follows that

(3) $$x\rho_t = y\rho_t \text{ , for all } t \in T.$$

Let A be a one-element space, $A = \{a\}$, and let $\alpha_1 : A \to X$ and $\alpha_2 : A \to X$ be defined as follows:

(4) $$a\alpha_1 = x; \quad a\alpha_2 = y.$$

Then $\alpha_1\rho_t = \alpha_2\rho_t$ for all $t \in T$, and it follows (proposition 1.1.12) that $\alpha_1 = \alpha_2$, which is absurd.

Secondly, μ is onto. For let $x^* = (x_t)_{t\in T}$ be an arbitrary point of X^*. Let $A = \{a\}$, as above, let $\alpha_t : A \to X_t$ map A onto $\{x_t\}$ for every $t \in T$, and let $\alpha \in K$ such that $\alpha\rho_t = \alpha_t$ for all $t \in T$. Then $(a\alpha)\mu = x^*$.

As X is compact, it follows that μ is a topological map. Consequently X^* is an object of $K^\theta(CZ)$; this, in its turn, implies that $\pi_t \in K^\theta(CZ)$ for all $t \in T$. Hence (according to lemma 3.2.2)

(5) $$\mathop{\mathbb{P}}_{t\in T} X_t = \prod_{t\in T} X_t \ (\pi_t),$$

as asserted.

3.2.5. PROPOSITION. In $K^\theta(CZ)$, a family of objects $(X_t)_{t\in T}$ admits a free join if and only if

(6) $$\prod_{t\in T} (1+\text{weight}(X_t)) \leq \aleph_\theta ;$$

this family of objects admits a direct join if and only if

(7) $$\text{card}\{t \in T : \text{weight}(X_t) > 1\} \leq \aleph_\theta .$$

PROOF. The first assertion follows from the contravariant correspondence between K(CZ) and K(BA) (the STONE duality theory); if A_t is the boolean algebra of all clopen subsets of X_t, then

(8) $$\aleph_0 \cdot \mathrm{card}(A_t) = \aleph_0 \cdot \mathrm{weight}(X_t)$$

and the STONE space of the direct product $\prod_{t \in T} A_t$ is a free join of $(X_t)_{t \in T}$ in K(CZ).

The second assertion is an immediate consequence of proposition 3.2.4 together with the following proposition (to be found in M.A. MAURICE [78,79]):

3.2.6. PROPOSITION. The weight of a topological product $\prod_{t \in T} X_t$ is at most $\aleph_\theta$ if and only if the following two conditions are both satisfied:

(i) $\mathrm{weight}(X_t) \leq \aleph_\theta$, for every $t \in T$;

(ii) $\mathrm{card}\{t \in T : \mathrm{weight}(X_t) > 1\} \leq \aleph_\theta$.

A topological sum of infinitely many compact spaces $X_t \neq \emptyset$ is not compact. However, if $\theta > 0$ a family of denumerably many one-point spaces does have a free join in K^θ(CZ), by proposition 3.2.5. Thus we find:

3.2.7. COROLLARY. If $0 < \theta \in$ ORD, K^θ(CZ) is not co-neat.

REMARK 1. We concluded from the existence of direct joins in K(BA), by means of the STONE duality theory, that free joins always exist in K(CZ). It is easy, in fact, to give an explicit description of such free joins.

Let $(X_t)_{t \in T}$ be an arbitrary family of objects of K(CZ). Let $\sum_{t \in T} X_t$ be a topological sum of $(X_t)_{t \in T}$, and let σ_t be the canonical embedding of X_t in this sum ($t \in T$). Then

(9) $$\beta\left(\sum_{t \in T} X_t\right) = \mathop{\ast}_{t \in T} X_t \ (\sigma_t),$$

where βX denotes the ČECH-STONE compactification of X (PH. DWINGER [31]).

3.2.8. PROPOSITION. K^θ(CR) is both neat and co-neat, for each $\theta \in$ ORD.

PROOF. We first prove that K^θ(CR) is neat. Suppose therefore that

(10) $$X = \prod_{t \in T} X_t(\rho_t)$$

in $K^{\theta}(CR)$. Obviously we may assume that $X_t \neq \emptyset$ for all $t \in T$. We will show that

(11) $$\text{card}\{t \in T : \text{weight}(X_t) > 1\} \leq \aleph_\theta ;$$

it then follows that the topological product $\prod_{t \in T} X_t$ is an object of $K^{\theta}(CR)$ (proposition 3.2.6) and hence (lemma 3.2.2) that it is a direct join of $(X_t)_{t \in T}$ with respect to the canonical projections $\pi_{t_o} : \prod_{t \in T} X_t \to X_{t_o}$.

Assume (11) to be false. Then

(12) $$\text{card}\{t \in T : U\rho_t \neq X_t\} > \aleph_\theta$$

for a suitable non-void open subset U of X. For suppose (12) is not true, for each open $U \neq \emptyset$. Let $\{U_\kappa\}_{\kappa < \aleph_\theta}$ be an open base for X, with all $U_\kappa \neq \emptyset$; for each $\kappa < \aleph_\theta$ we put

(13) $$T_\kappa = \{t \in T : U_\kappa \rho_t \neq X_t\} .$$

By assumption, $\text{card}(T_\kappa) \leq \aleph_\theta$, for every $\kappa < \aleph_\theta$. Hence if

(14) $$S = \{t \in T : \text{weight}(X_t) > 1\} \setminus \bigcup_{\kappa < \aleph_\theta} T_\kappa ,$$

then $\text{card}(S) > \aleph_\theta$; thus in any case $S \neq \emptyset$. Let $t \in S$; then $U_\kappa \rho_t = X_t$ for all $\kappa < \aleph_\theta$, and it follows that $U\rho_t = X_t$ for every open set U in X. This contradicts the fact that $\text{weight}(X_t) > 1$.

Now we show that the assumption that (11) is false leads to a contradiction. Let U be a non-void open subset of X, and let $\{t_n : n \in N\}$ be a denumerable subset of T (with $t_n \neq t_m$ if $n \neq m$) such that

(15) $$U\rho_{t_n} \neq X_{t_n}$$

for all $n \in N$. Let Y be the Cantor discontinuum, $y \in Y$, and let $\{V_n\}_{n \in N}$ be a sequence of clopen neighbourhoods of y such that

(16) $$\bigcap_{n \in N} V_n = \{y\} .$$

For each $n \in N$ we construct a continuous map $\alpha_{t_n} : Y \to X_{t_n}$ in the following manner: let

(17) $$x'_{t_n} \in U\rho_{t_n} \; ; \; x''_{t_n} \in X_{t_n} \setminus U\rho_{t_n} \; ;$$

and let α_{t_n} map V_n onto $\{x'_{t_n}\}$ and $Y \setminus V_n$ onto $\{x''_{t_n}\}$. If $t \in T$ is not one of the t_n, then let α_t be an arbitrary continuous map $Y \to X_t$.

As $(\rho_t)_{t \in T}$ is a direct join, with X as its source, there exists a continuous map $\alpha : Y \to X$ such that $\alpha \circ \rho_t = \alpha_t$ for all $t \in T$. It follows that

(18) $$U\alpha^{-1} \subset (U\rho_t)\rho_t^{-1}\alpha^{-1} \subset (U\rho_t)\alpha_t^{-1};$$

hence

(19) $$U\alpha^{-1} \subset \bigcap_{n \in N} (U\rho_{t_n})\alpha_{t_n}^{-1} = \bigcap_{n \in N} V_n = \{y\} .$$

Consequently y has to be an isolated point in Y; this is absurd.

Thus we have indeed shown that $K^{\theta}(CR)$ is neat. We next turn to a proof of its co-neatness.

Suppose $X = \mathop{\ast}_{t \in T} X_t \; (\rho_t)$ in K. We assert that all ρ_t are 1-1 maps, and that

(20) $$\overline{X_t\rho_t} \cap \overline{\bigcup_{\substack{s \in T \\ s \neq t}} X_s\rho_s} = \emptyset,$$

for every $t \in T$.

In order to prove this, we consider a space $Y = X_t \cup \{a\}$, where $a \notin X_t$ and where the topology of Y is the sum of the topology of X_t and the (discrete) topology of $\{a\}$. Let α_t denote the identity map $X_t \to Y$, and let α_s map X_s onto $\{a\}$, for each $s \in T \setminus \{t\}$. There exists a continuous map $\alpha : X \to Y$ such that $\rho_s \circ \alpha = \alpha_s$, for all $s \in T$; from this fact our assertion readily follows.

It also follows that each $\rho_t : X_t \to X_t\rho_t$ is bicontinuous. In fact, its inverse apparently coincides with the continuous map $\alpha | X_t\rho_t$.

We conclude that the subspace $\bigcup_{t \in T} X_t\rho_t$ of X is a topological sum of the spaces X_t, $t \in T$. As it is also a completely regular space of weight at most $\aleph_\theta$, i.e. an object of $K^{\theta}(CR)$, it follows from lemma 3.2.3 that $\bigcup_{t \in T} X_t\rho_t$ is a free join (in fact, it is easily seen that

(21) $$\bigcup_{t \in T} X_t\rho_t = X,$$

so that X itself turns out to be a topological sum of $(X_t)_{t \in T}$.

REMARK 2. It is much easier to show that the category K(CR) (no restrictions on the weight) is neat: this follows at once from lemma 3.2.2. The same holds for K(CZ); but it is not true anymore for K(M) and K(ZM), as in these categories topological products not always exist.

3.2.9. COROLLARY. In $K^\theta(CR)$, a family of objects $(X_t)_{t \in T}$ admits a direct join if and only if either an $X_t = \emptyset$ or all $X_t \neq \emptyset$ and (7) holds; and it admits a free join if and only if

(22) $$\operatorname{card}\{t \in T : X_t \neq \emptyset\} \leqq \aleph_\theta .$$

3.2.10. PROPOSITION. Every category $K^\theta(M)$ or $K^\theta(ZM)$, $\theta \in$ ORD, is both neat and co-neat.

PROOF. The fact that these categories are co-neat is proved in the same way as for the categories $K^\theta(CR)$.

The proof of the neatness of $K^\theta(M)$ and $K^\theta(ZM)$ is an easy adaptation from the corresponding part of the proof of proposition 3.2.8. Let K be one of the categories $K^\theta(M)$, $K^\theta(ZM)$, and let $X = \prod_{t \in T} X_t(\rho_t)$ in K. If one of the X_t is empty, then the topological product $\emptyset = \mathbb{P}_{t \in T} X_t$ obviously is a direct join. Suppose therefore that $X_t \neq \emptyset$ for every $t \in T$.

If

(23) $$\operatorname{card}\{t \in T : \operatorname{weight}(X_t) > 1\} \leqq \aleph_0 ,$$

then the topological product $\mathbb{P}_{t \in T} X_t$ is an object of K and hence is the source of a direct join. Suppose (23) is false. Then, using the fact that in X the first axiom of countability is satisfied, one shows as in the proof of 3.2.8 that there exists a non-void open set U in X such that

(24) $$\operatorname{card}\{t \in T : U\rho_t \neq X_t\} > \aleph_0 .$$

From this one deduces (exactly as in the proof of proposition 3.2.8) that all points of the Cantor discontinuum are isolated, which is absurd.

3.2.11. COROLLARY. Let K be one of the categories $K^{\theta}(M)$ or $K^{\theta}(ZM)$, $\theta \in$ ORD. A family of objects $(X_t)_{t \in T}$ in K has a direct join in K if and only if either an $X_t = \emptyset$ or all $X_t \neq \emptyset$ and (23) holds; it admits a free join in K if and only if (22) is satisfied.

3.2.12. PROPOSITION. $K^{\theta}(H)$ is neat, for every $\theta \in$ ORD.

PROOF. Suppose $X = \prod_{t \in T} X_t \; (\rho_t)$ in H. Obviously we may assume that $X_t \neq \emptyset$ for every $t \in T$. We will show that then

$$\text{card}\,\{ t \in T : X_t \neq \{0\}\} < \aleph_0. \tag{25}$$

Assume (25) to be false; let $t_n \in T$, for each $n \in N$, such that $X_{t_n} \neq \emptyset$; we take care that $t_n \neq t_m$ for $n \neq m$. Let Y be a one-dimensional euclidean space, and for each $n \in N$ let α_{t_n} be a bounded linear operator $Y \to X_{t_n}$ with $\|\alpha_{t_n}\| = n\,\|\rho_{t_n}\|$. There exists a bounded linear operator $\alpha : Y \to X$ such that $\alpha \circ \rho_{t_n} = \alpha_{t_n}$, for all $n \in N$. It follows that

$$n \cdot \|\rho_{t_n}\| = \|\alpha_{t_n}\| = \|\alpha \circ \rho_{t_n}\| \leqq \|\alpha\|\,\|\rho_{t_n}\| \tag{26}$$

for every $n \in N$. Now it is easily verified that every ρ_t is onto; consequently $\|\rho_{t_n}\| \neq 0$, and we arrive at the absurdity: $\|\alpha\| \geqq n$ for every $n \in N$. Thus (25) is proved.

From (25) it follows that the topological product of all X_t coincides with the Hilbert sum

$$X^{*} = \bigoplus_{t \in T} X_t, \tag{27}$$

and that X^{*} is an object of $K^{\theta}(H)$. As obviously X^{*} serves as a direct join of $(X_t)_{t \in T}$, it follows that $K^{\theta}(H)$ is neat.

As a corollary to the proof we obtain:

3.2.13. COROLLARY. Let $\theta \in$ ORD. A family $(X_t)_{t \in T}$ of objects of $K^{\theta}(H)$ has a direct join in $K^{\theta}(H)$ if and only if either some $X_t = \emptyset$ or all $X_t \neq \emptyset$ and (25) holds.

3.2.14. PROPOSITION. Let $\theta \in$ ORD. A family $(X_t)_{t\in T}$ of objects of $K^{\theta}(H)$ has a free join in $K^{\theta}(H)$ if and only if the following set S is finite:

(28) $$S = \{ t \in T : \operatorname{card}(X_t) > 1 \} .$$

If this is the case, the Hilbert sum $X^{*} = \bigoplus_{t\in S} X_t$ is a free join,

(29) $$\bigoplus_{t\in S} X_t = \mathop{\ast}_{t\in T} X_t\ (\sigma_t),$$

where σ_t is the natural injection $X_t \to \bigoplus_{s\in S} X_s$ if $t \in S$; σ_t is the empty map if $X_t = \emptyset$; and σ_t maps X_t onto the zero element of X^{*} if $X_t = \{0\}$.

PROOF. Let $X = \mathop{\ast}_{t\in T} X_t\ (\rho_t)$, and suppose S is infinite. Let $(t_n)_{n\in N}$ be a sequence of pairwise distinct elements of S. Let Y be a one-dimensional euclidean space; for each $n \in N$, let α_n be a bounded linear operator of X_{t_n} onto Y with $\| \alpha_n \| = n.\| \rho_{t_n} \|$. Then every bounded linear operator $\alpha : X \to Y$ satisfying $\rho_{t_n} \circ \alpha = \alpha_{t_n}$ for all $n \in N$, also satisfies $\|\alpha\| \geq n$ for all $n \in N$, which is contradictory.

Hence S is finite. But then (29) is easily shown to be valid.

3.2.15. COROLLARY. $K^{\theta}(H)$ is not co-neat, for every choice of $\theta \in$ ORD.

3.2.16. PROPOSITION. The category K(CMoG) is neat.

PROOF. Suppose $X = \prod_{t\in T} X_t\ (\rho_t)$ in K(CMoG). Let X^{*} denote the topological direct product

(30) $$X^{*} = \mathop{\mathbb{P}}_{t\in T} X_t;$$

we will show that X^{*} is an object of K.

Let the map $\mu : X \to X^{*}$ be defined by (2); clearly μ is a continuous homomorphism. We will show that μ is 1-1.

Suppose this were not the case; then there would exist an $x \neq 1$ in X such that $x\mu = 1$ (we denote both the neutral element of X and the neutral element of X^{*} by 1). Let Y be the closure of the subgroup of X generated by x; Y is again a compact monothetic group. If α_1 is the identity map of Y into X and if $\alpha_2 : Y \to X$ maps every element of Y onto 1, then $\alpha_1\rho_t = \alpha_2\rho_t$ for all $t \in T$; hence $\alpha_1 = \alpha_2$ (by proposition 1.1.9); this is contradictory.

As X is compact, it follows that μ is a topological isomorphism of X into X^{**}. We will finish the proof by showing that μ is onto.

Take an arbitrary point $x^{**} = (x_t)_{t\in T} \in X$. According to proposition 1.4.22, K(CMoG) has a dually universal object M. Let a be a generator of a dense subgroup of M; for each $t \in T$ there exists a continuous homomorphism $\alpha_t : M \to X_t$ such that $a\alpha_t = x_t$. Then $(a\alpha)\rho_t = a\alpha_t = x_t$, for all $t \in T$; i.e. $(a\alpha)\mu = x^{**}$.

REMARK 3. K(CMoG) is not co-neat, as is shown by the following example. Let X_2 and X_3 be the character groups of $Z(2^\infty)$ and $Z(3^\infty)$. As $Z(2^\infty)$ and $Z(3^\infty)$ are subgroups of T_d (the circle group with discrete topology), X_2 and X_3 are compact monothetic groups. So is the character group X of $Z(2^\infty) \times Z(3^\infty)$; moreover, X is the topological direct product of X_2 and X_3. It is easily seen that X is a free join of X_2 and X_3, although obviously it is not a topological direct sum.

REMARK 4. From proposition 3.2.16 a complete characterization can be obtained of all families $(X_t)_{t\in T}$ of objects of K(CMoG) which admit a direct join. Let G_t be the character group of X_t, for every $t \in T$. It follows from proposition 3.2.16 that a direct join of $(X_t)_{t\in T}$ exists in K(CMoG) if and only if the topological direct product $\prod_{t\in T} X_t$ is a compact monothetic group, and this is the case if and only if the direct sum (restricted direct product) of the groups G_t is isomorphic to a subgroup of T_d. From this together with the fact that T_d is isomorphic to a direct sum of continuously many copies of Q_d and of one copy each of the groups $Z(p^\infty)$, p prime, a necessary and sufficient condition for the groups G_t, and hence also for the groups X_t, can be distilled.

3.3. The embedding theorem for topological spaces

The main result of this section is the following: if K is a neat category of topological spaces, then the monomorphisms $(f)EMB_{K,F,x}$ are what they ought to be: topological embedding maps. This leads to variants of the fundamental embedding theorem of section 2.3

and of the existence theorems of section 2.4 that are more suitable for categories of topological spaces.

Although there are not many applications, we derive - for completeness' sake - a theorem on the existence of topologically dually universal (systems of) morphisms in co-neat categories; as co-neatness is not the category-theoretical dual of neatness, a separate proof is necessary.

If X is a topological space and A a set, then X^A will designate the topological product $\prod_{\alpha \in A} X_\alpha$, with $X_\alpha = X$ for all $\alpha \in A$ (i.e. the function space X^A with the weak topology); for each $\alpha_0 \in A$, the map $(x_\alpha)_{\alpha \in A} \to x_{\alpha_0}$ will be denoted by π_{α_0}.

We will say that a map $\varphi : A \to B$ is of finite multiplicity if $(\beta)\varphi^{-1}$ is finite for every $\beta \in B$. A map ϕ of a topological space X into a topological space Y is called open if φ is open, considered as a map $X \to X\varphi$. Under these conventions, we have:

3.3.1. PROPOSITION. Let A,B be sets, and let $\phi \in B^A$. For every topological space X, the map $\phi^* : X^B \to X^A$, defined by

(1) $$\phi^* \circ \pi_\alpha = \pi_{\alpha\varphi}, \text{ for all } \alpha \in A,$$

is continuous. If $\varphi : A \to B$ is of finite multiplicity, then ϕ^* is also open. In particular, if φ is a 1-1 map of A onto B, then ϕ^* is a topological map of X^B onto X^A.

PROOF: obvious.

3.3.2. TOPOLOGICAL EMBEDDING THEOREM. Let X and Y be topological spaces, μ a topological map of Y into X, F a semigroup with unit and f a homomorphism of F into the semigroup of all continuous maps $Y \to Y$, sending the unit element ε of F onto i_Y. The map $\hat{f} : Y \to X^F$, defined by

(2) $$\hat{f} \circ \pi_\phi = (\phi f) \circ \mu,$$

for every $\phi \in F$, is a topological embedding. Moreover, if we define for every $\phi_0 \in F$ a map $\phi_0^* : X^F \to X^F$, in the usual way:

(3) $$\varphi_0^* \circ \pi_\phi = \pi_{\phi_0 \cdot \phi},$$

for every $\phi \in F$, then

(4) $$\hat{f} \circ \phi^{*} = (\phi f) \circ \hat{f}$$

for all $\phi \in F$.

PROOF. The proof is similar to the proof of theorem 2.3.7; the only thing that must be added is a proof of the fact that $\hat{f}$ is topological. But this is immediate: we need only remark that $\hat{f} : Y \to Y\hat{f}$ has as its inverse the continuous map $(\pi_{\varepsilon}|Y\hat{f}) \circ \mu^{-1}$, where μ^{-1} is the inverse of the map $Y \to Y\mu$.

3.3.3. PROPOSITION. Let K be a neat category of topological spaces. Let X,Y be objects of K, and let $\mu : Y \to X$ be a topological map. Furthermore, let f be a homomorphism of a semigroup F into H(Y,Y). Then for each $Z \in \Delta(X,F)$ the map $(f,\mu)\mathrm{EMB}_{K,F,Z}$ is topological.

PROOF. This follows from the theorems 3.3.2 and 2.2.10.

3.3.4. THEOREM. Let K be a neat category of topological spaces, and suppose that K satisfies condition VIII_0 of 1.3.7. Let K_0 be a subcategory of K. Then K contains topologically K_0-universal morphisms and bimorphisms if and only if it contains a topologically K_0-universal object. Similarly, if VIII_{θ} holds in K for some $\theta \in \mathrm{ORD}$, then K contains topologically $(K_0,\aleph_{\theta})$-universal semigroups of morphisms and groups of bimorphisms if and only if it contains a topologically K_0-universal object.

PROOF. This is implied by the previous proposition, taking for X a topologically K_0-universal object and for F a free (semi-)group.

It follows that the results in section 2.5 dealing with universal morphisms in categories of topological spaces (sc. the propositions 2.5.9 to 2.5.14, 2.5.19 to 2.5.22) can all be strengthened to assert that topologically universal (systems of) morphisms or bimorphisms exist.

The argument leading up to theorem 3.3.4 can be dualized. Let X be a topological space, and let F be a semigroup. If we consider F as a discrete space, the topological product $X \times F$ is at the same time a topological sum of as many copies of X as there are elements of F. For each $\phi \in F$, let σ_ϕ denote the following map $X \to X \times F$:

(5) $$x\sigma_\phi = (x,\phi), \text{ for all } x \in X.$$

Every σ_ϕ is a topological injection of X into $X \times F$.

If $\phi_o \in F$, we denote by ${}^*\phi_o$ the map $X \times F \to X \times F$ satisfying

(6) $$\sigma_\phi \circ {}^*\phi_o = \sigma_{\phi\phi_o},$$

for all $\phi \in F$. That is, $(x,\phi)\phi_o = (x, \phi\phi_o)$ for arbitrary $(x,\phi) \in X \times F$. Then $\phi \to {}^*\phi$ is an isomorphism of F onto a semigroup ${}^*F$ of continuous maps $X \times F \to X \times F$.

Suppose now ν is a continuous map of X onto Y, and let f be a homomorphism of F into the semigroup of all continuous maps $Y \to Y$. Let us denote by $\check{f}$ the map $X \times F \to Y$, satisfying

(7) $$\sigma_\phi \circ \check{f} = \nu \circ (\phi f),$$

for all $\phi \in F$. In other words, if $(x,\phi) \in X \times F$, then

(8) $$(x,\phi)\check{f} = (x\nu)(\phi f).$$

Clearly $\check{f}$ is a continuous map of $X \times F$ onto Y; moreover

(9) $${}^*\phi \circ \check{f} = \check{f} \circ (\phi f),$$

for every $\phi \in F$.

Thus we obtain the following "dual" to theorem 3.3.4:

3.3.5. THEOREM. Let K be a co-neat category of topological spaces, and suppose every denumerable family of objects of K has a free join in K. Let K_o be a subcategory of K. Then K contains topologically dually K_o-universal morphisms and bimorphisms if and only if it admits a topologically dually K_o-universal object.

Similarly, if $\theta \in$ ORD and if every family of at most $\aleph_\theta$ objects of K admits a free join in K, then K contains topologically dually $(K_o, \aleph_\theta)$-universal semigroups of morphisms and groups of bimorphisms as soon as it contains a topologically dually universal object.

Consequently, proposition 2.5.25 can also be strengthened, in the sense that a category $K^{\theta}(CR)$ or $K^{\theta}(ZM)$ will contain topologically dually universal morphisms and bimorphisms as soon as it contains a topologically dually universal object.

3.4. Applications

This section contains several results obtained by means of the constructions leading to the fundamental embedding theorem and its strengthened version for neat categories. In the considerations below we no longer restrict these constructions to properly defined categories, applying them now to individual spaces too. Moreover, we also derive a number of results that are not of the nature of existence theorems on universal or dually universal morphisms, such as a generalization of a theorem of R.D. ANDERSON on raising of self-maps of compact metrizable spaces to self-maps of the Cantor discontinuum, or such as a slight strengthening of a theorem of J. DE GROOT and R.H. MC.DOWELL on the possibility of obtaining countable metrizable groups as continuous isomorphic images of groups of homeomorphisms of the Cantor set.

3.4.1. DEFINITION. Let X and Y be topological spaces. Two continuous maps $\phi : X \to X$ and $\psi : Y \to Y$ are called equivalent if there exists a topological map τ of X onto Y such that $\psi = \tau^{-1} \circ \phi \circ \tau$.

(1)
$$\begin{array}{ccc} X & \xrightarrow{\ \phi\ } & X \\ \downarrow \tau & & \downarrow \tau \\ Y & \xrightarrow{\ \psi\ } & Y \end{array}$$

3.4.2. DEFINITION. Let X,Y be topological spaces, and let $\phi : X \to X$ and $\psi : Y \to Y$ be continuous. We say that ψ can be raised or lifted to ϕ if there exists a continuous map τ of X onto Y such that $\tau\psi = \phi\tau$.

From the considerations in the previous section we derive at once the following two propositions:

3.4.3. PROPOSITION. Let X be a topological space, and suppose X is homeomorphic to a topological product $Y^{\aleph_0}$. Then there exists an autohomeomorphism Φ of X (a continuous self-map Ψ of X) with the property that every possible autohomeomorphism (continuous self-map) of an arbitrary subspace of X is equivalent to a suitable restriction of

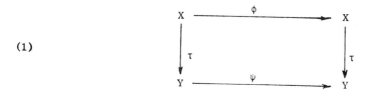

Φ (of Ψ, respectively).

Examples of spaces X which are homeomorphic to a product $Y^{\aleph_0}$ are the Cantor discontinuum, all generalized Cantor discontinua, the space of all irrational numbers with the topology induced by the topology of the real numbers (this space is homeomorphic to $N^{\aleph_0}$; cf. [70], Vol.I, §14 V), the Hilbert fundamental cube, all Tychonov cubes of transfinite weight, the infinite torus $T^{\aleph_0}$, etc.

REMARK 1. A space X obviously is homeomorphic to a topological product $Y^{\aleph_0}$ if and only if X is homeomorphic to $X^{\aleph_0}$.

REMARK 2. Let X be a topological space, homeomorphic to a denumerable topological product $Y^{\aleph_0}$. Our constructions indicate that the bilateral shift $\Phi: X^I \to X^I$, such that

(2) $$(\xi_k)_{k \in I}\Phi = (\xi_{k+1})_{k \in I},$$

is (equivalent to) a universal autohomeomorphism for X.

R.D. ANDERSON pointed out to us that it is possible to describe Φ in a different way. Let A be an arbitrary denumerable set. Then X^I is homeomorphic to the space $Y^{A\times I}$, and hence also to $Y^{I\times A}$. If we identify X^I with $Y^{I\times A}$, the action of Φ can be expressed in the form

(3) $$(\eta_{k,\alpha})_{k \in I,\alpha \in A}\Phi = (\eta_{k+1,\alpha})_{k \in I,\alpha \in A}.$$

Let $Z = Y^I$, and let $\Phi_o : Z \to Z$ be the bilateral shift with base Y:

(4) $$(\eta_k)_{k \in I}\Phi_o = (\eta_{k+1})_{k \in I},$$

for arbitrary $\zeta = (\eta_k)_{k \in I} \in Z$. If we now identify $Y^{I\times A}$ with Z^A, it turns out that Φ is equivalent to the autohomeomorphism $\Phi_o^A : Z^A \to Z^A$ such that

(5) $$(\zeta_\alpha)_{\alpha \in A}\Phi_o^A = (\zeta_\alpha\Phi_o)_{\alpha \in A}$$

for arbitrary $z = (\zeta_\alpha)_{\alpha \in A} \in Z^A$.

Similarly the unilateral shift on X^N, which is a universal continuous self-map, can be split up in a "product" of denumerably many copies of the unilateral shift on Y^N.

Thus, for instance, a universal autohomeomorphism of the Cantor discontinuum C is obtainable as the "product" of a denumerable number of copies of the bilateral shift on $\{0,1\}^I$. This is of interest, as the bilateral shift with {0,1} as base space has been extensively studied (see e.g. W.H. GOTTSCHALK and G.A. HEDLUND [45], section 12).

3.4.4. PROPOSITION. Let X be a topological space, and suppose X is homeomorphic to a topological sum of $\aleph_0$ copies of a space Y. Then there exists an autohomeomorphism Φ of X (a continuous self-map Ψ of X) with the following property. If Z is any continuous image of X, then every possible autohomeomorphism (continuous self-map) of Z can be raised to Φ (to Ψ, respectively).

Examples of spaces X which are homeomorphic to a topological sum of $\aleph_0$ copies of a space Y (or equivalently, which are homeomorphic to a topological sum of $\aleph_0$ copies of X itself) are the space of all rational numbers with its usual topology, the space of all irrational numbers, the open Cantor discontinuum (i.e. the Cantor discontinuum minus one point), all infinite discrete spaces, etc.

Every separable complete metric space is a continuous image of the space of all irrational numbers (cf. [70], Vol.I, §32,II). More generally, every Souslin space is a continuous image of the space of irrationals (by a Souslin space we mean a topological space which is a continuous image of a separable, metrizable, and metrically topologically complete space). Hence we have:

3.4.5. COROLLARY. There exists an autohomeomorphism Φ (a continuous self-map Ψ) of the space of irrational numbers to which every autohomeomorphism (continuous self-map, respectively) of an arbitrary Souslin space can be raised.

The class of Souslin spaces comprises not only all separable complete metric spaces, but also all Borel subsets and even all analytic subsets of separable complete metric spaces (see e.g. [70] and [114]).

Every σ-compact metrizable space is a continuous image of the open Cantor discontinuum (this follows easily from the fact that every compact metrizable space is a continuous image of the Cantor set; cf. the notes to chapter 1). Hence:

3.4.6. COROLLARY. There exists an autohomeomorphism (a continuous self-map) of the open Cantor discontinuum to which every autohomeomorphism (continuous self-map, respectively) of an arbitrary σ-compact metrizable space can be raised.

Every denumerable non-compact metrizable space may be mapped continuously on every countable metrizable space (J. DE GROOT [45*], theorem IV). In particular, every countable metrizable space is a continuous image of the space of all rational numbers. Hence, from proposition 3.4.4:

3.4.7. COROLLARY. There exists an autohomeomorphism Φ (a continuous self-map Ψ) of the space of rational numbers, to which every autohomeomorphism (every continuous self-map, respectively) of an arbitrary countable metrizable space can be raised.

REMARK 3. Let Ξ be a class of topological spaces. We will denote by $\Xi\Pi$ ($\Xi\Sigma$) the class of all spaces Y which are homeomorphic to a topological product (a topological sum, respectively) of $\aleph_0$ copies of a space $X \in \Xi$. Whenever Ξ stands for the class of all topological spaces we will omit it; i.e. in that case we write Σ, $\Sigma\Pi$, $\Pi\Sigma$ etc. instead of $\Xi\Sigma$, $\Xi\Sigma\Pi$, $\Xi\Pi\Sigma$, respectively. Furthermore we will use (within the confines of this remark) the notation $X \equiv Y$ to indicate that the topological spaces X and Y are homeomorphic to each other.

For all $X \in \Pi$ there exist topologically universal autohomeomorphisms and continuous self-maps (proposition 3.4.3). (More exactly, the category K of all continuous self-maps of X contains topologically universal morphisms and bimorphisms). Similarly all $X \in \Sigma$ have dually universal autohomeomorphisms and self-maps (proposition 3.4.4). It follows that in all spaces $X \in \Pi \cap \Sigma$ there exist both topologically universal autohomeomorphisms (continuous self-maps) and topologically dually universal ones.

It is therefore of interest to note that

$$\Pi \cap \Sigma = \Sigma\Pi . \tag{6}$$

In fact, $\Sigma \cap \Pi \subset \Sigma\Pi$, for if $X \in \Sigma \cap \Pi$, then $X \equiv X \times I$ and $X \equiv X^I$, and hence

(7) $$X \cong (X \times I)^{I} \in \Sigma\Pi .$$

Clearly $\Sigma\Pi \subset \Pi$. And $\Sigma\Pi \subset \Sigma$, for if $X \in \Sigma\Pi$, say

(8) $$X \cong (Y \times I)^{I},$$

then

(9) $$X \cong (Y \times I)^{I} \times (Y \times I) \cong ((Y \times I)^{I} \times Y) \times I \in \Sigma .$$

The simplest non-degenerate example of a space $X \in \Pi \cap \Sigma$ is the space of all irrational numbers: this space can be obtained from a one-point space Y by applying first the Σ-operation and next the Π-operation. Other examples are the topological product of the space of all irrationals with the Hilbert fundamental cube, or with the infinite torus. Generally: if $X \in \Pi$ and $Y \in \Sigma\Pi$, then $X \times Y \in \Sigma\Pi$. Indeed:

(10) $$X \times Y \cong X^{I} \times Y^{I} \cong (X \times Y)^{I} \in \Pi$$

and

(11) $$X \times Y \cong X \times (Y \times I) \cong (X \times Y) \times I \in \Sigma .$$

(We observe in addition that it is easily seen that the classes Σ, Π, $\Sigma\Pi$ and $\Pi\Sigma$ are all distinct, and that no new classes can be obtained by applying Π or Σ again).

3.4.8. DEFINITION. Let X be a completely regular space, and let S be a set of continuous self-maps of X. A compact space X' is called an <u>S-compactification</u> of X if there exists a topological map τ of X onto a dense subspace of X' such that every map $\tau^{-1} \circ \sigma \circ \tau: X\tau \to X\tau$ ($\sigma \in S$) can be continuously extended to a map $\sigma' : X' \to X'$.

3.4.9. PROPOSITION. Let $\theta \in$ ORD, let X be a completely regular space of weight at most $\aleph_\theta$, and let G be a semigroup of continuous self-maps of X with card(G) $\leqq \aleph_\theta$. Then there exists a G-compactification X' of X with weight at most $\aleph_\theta$.

PROOF. Let F be a topologically ($\aleph_\theta$)-universal semigroup of morphisms in K^{θ}(CR); its existence is warranted by theorem 3.3.4 together with proposition 3.2.7. Say $F \subset H(U,U)$, where $U = [0,1]^{\aleph_\theta}$ is compact. Then there exists a topological map $\tau: X \to U$ such that every $\gamma \in G$ is equivalent to a map $\phi|X\tau$. It follows that the closure of $X\tau$ in U is a G-compactification of X.

Proposition 3.4.9 can be immediately sharpened to the following theorem:

3.4.10. THEOREM. Let X be a completely regular space, and let S be a set of continuous maps $\sigma : X \to X$. Then there exists an S-compactification X' of X such that

(12) $$\text{weight}(X') \leq \aleph_0 . \text{card}(S) . \text{weight}(X).$$

3.4.11. COROLLARY (J. DE GROOT and R.H. MCDOWELL [51]). If X is a separable metrizable space and if S is countable, X has a metrizable S-compactification.

If we make use of proposition 2.5.20 we obtain similarly:

3.4.12. COROLLARY. If X is a zero-dimensional separable metrizable space, and if S is countable, X has a zero-dimensional metrizable S-compactification.

REMARK 4. Let X' be an S-compactification of X;without loss of generality we may assume that X' contains X as a dense subset in such a way that every $\sigma \in S$ is the restriction to X of a continuous map $\sigma' : X' \to X'$. Then, as X is dense, σ' is uniquely determined by σ; moreover, all algebraic relations between elements σ_i of S also hold between the corresponding elements σ_i'. In particular, if σ is a retraction of X (i.e. if $\sigma^2 = \sigma$), then σ' will be a retraction of X'; if σ is of order 2, $\sigma^2 = i_X$, then $(\sigma')^2 = i_{X'}$, etc. In general, if S is a (semi-)group, so is $S' = \{\sigma' : \sigma \in S\}$, and $\sigma \to \sigma'$ is an isomorphism of S onto S'.

A different way to arrive at this is the following. For our present purposes we are not interested in <u>universal</u> systems of morphisms; hence there is no reason for working with a free semigroup or group in the constructions of section 2.4. If instead we use a star functor constructed by means of the semigroup or group generated by S, we arrive at once at a compactifying semigroup S' which is isomorphic with S.

3.4.13. COROLLARY. Every topological group G can be topologically embedded as a dense subset in a compact Hausdorff space X in such a way that all left and right translations in G can be extended to autohomeomorphisms of X. This can be done in such a manner that the weight of X equals max {card(G), weight(G)} .

3.4.14. COROLLARY. Every topological semigroup G can be topologically embedded as a dense subset in a compact Hausdorff space X in such a way that all left and right translations in G can be extended to continuous self-maps of X. The space X can be made to satisfy the additional requirement: weight(X) = max{card(G), weight(G)} .

In particular, if G is a countable metrizable group, the space X can be taken to be compact metrizable (cf. [51] , corollary 2.8).

From corollary 3.4.12 we obtain similarly:

3.4.15. COROLLARY. Every countable zero-dimensional metrizable topological group G (semigroup S) can be topologically embedded as a dense subset in a zero-dimensional compact metrizable space X, in such a way that all left and right translations of G can be extended to autohomeomorphisms (continuous self-maps, respectively) of X.

3.4.16. LEMMA. Let G be a topological group and suppose the space G is a dense subspace of a compact Hausdorff space X. Furthermore, suppose that for each $\gamma \in G$ there exists an autohomeomorphism γ' of X extending right translation over γ in G: $(\gamma_0)\gamma' = \gamma_0 \cdot \gamma$, for every $\gamma_0 \in G$. Then the map $h : \gamma' \to \gamma$ is a continuous isomorphism of the group $G' = \{\gamma' : \gamma \in G\}$, furnished with the topology of uniform convergence, onto G.

PROOF. Let the neutral element of G be designated by ε, and let U be an arbitrary open neighbourhood of ε. Let V be an open subset of X such that $V \cap G = U$, and let V_0 be an open subset of X such that $\varepsilon \in V_0$ and $\overline{V}_0 \subset U$.

The set

$$W = (V \times V) \cup ((X \setminus V_0) \times (X \setminus V_0)) \tag{13}$$

is a neighbourhood of the diagonal $\Delta = \{(x,x) : x \in X\}$ in $X \times X$; hence the set

(14) $$S = \{\gamma' \in G' : (x, x\gamma') \in W \text{ for all } x \in X\}$$

is a neighbourhood of the identity i_X of G' in the topology of uniform convergence. As obviously Sh = U, it follows that h is continuous.

3.4.17. PROPOSITION. Every topological group G is the image under a continuous isomorphism of a group G' of autohomeomorphisms of a compact Hausdorff space X, furnished with the topology of uniform convergence. The space X can be made to satisfy: weight(X) = = max{card(G), weight(G)}. If G is zero-dimensional, X can be chosen to be zero-dimensional too.

PROOF. All assertions follow readily from corollaries 3.4.13, 3.4.14, 3.4.15 and lemma 3.4.16.

It is an open problem whether $K^{o}(CZ)$ contains dually universal morphisms or bimorphisms (problem 1 in section 2.5). However, R.D. ANDERSON [4] has shown that at least every autohomeomorphism or continuous self-map of an arbitrary compact metrizable space X can be raised to the Cantor set. We will present below a different proof, based on the direct product constructions used in chapter 2 in order to obtain universal morphisms; at the same time we extend ANDERSON's theorem to countable systems of mappings:

3.4.18. THEOREM. Countably many autohomeomorphisms (continuous self-maps) of a compact metrizable space X can always be simultaneously raised to autohomeomorphisms (continuous self-maps) of the Cantor discontinuum C.

In fact, we will prove somewhat more:

3.4.19. THEOREM. Let S be a countable system of autohomeomorphisms (continuous self-maps) of a compact metrizable space X. Then there exist a system $\overline{S}$ of autohomeomorphisms (continuous self-maps) of the Cantor discontinuum C, a 1-1 map $\sigma \to \overline{\sigma}$ of S onto $\overline{S}$, which is an open map if both S and $\overline{S}$ are furnished with the topology of uniform convergence, and a continuous map τ of C onto X, such that $\overline{\sigma}\tau = \tau\sigma$, for all $\sigma \in S$.

(15)
$$\begin{array}{ccc} C & \xrightarrow{\ \bar{\sigma}\ } & C \\ \downarrow{\scriptstyle\tau} & & \downarrow{\scriptstyle\tau} \\ X & \xrightarrow[\ \sigma\ ]{} & X \end{array}$$

PROOF. We only treat the case of a countable set S of autohomeomorphisms $\sigma : X \to X$, the case of continuous self-maps being entirely similar.

If X is a zero-dimensional space, the situation is extremely simple. For then the topological product $X \times C$ is homeomorphic to C; let ρ be the usual projection $X \times C \to X$, and for each $\sigma \in S$ let $\sigma' : X \times C \to X \times C$ be defined by

(16) $$(x,c)\sigma' = (x\sigma, c),$$

for arbitrary $x \in X$ and $c \in C$. Then always $\sigma' \circ \rho = \rho \circ \sigma$, and it is immediately verified that the map $\sigma' \to \sigma$ is continuous if S and $S' = \{\sigma' : \sigma \in S\}$ are provided with the topology of uniform convergence.

Next, let X be an arbitrary compact metrizable space. Let F be the group generated by S; by what we have shown already it suffices to raise every $\phi \in F$ to an autohomeomorphism $\bar{\phi}$ of a zero-dimensional compact metrizable space Y, by means of one single continuous map τ of Y onto X, in such a way that the map $\phi \to \bar{\phi}$ is open.

For each $\phi_o \in F$ we define $\phi_o^* : X^F \to X^F$ in the usual way: $\phi_o^* \circ \pi_\phi = \pi_{\phi_o\phi}$, for each canonical projection $\pi_\phi : X^F \to X$; and we define the topological embedding $\mu : X \to X^F$ (again: as usual) through the condition: $\mu \circ \pi_\phi = \phi$, for all $\phi \in F$.

Similarly for each $\phi_o \in F$ we define $\phi_o^+ : C^F \to C^F$ by the condition: $\phi_o^+ \circ \pi'_\phi = \pi'_{\phi_o\phi}$ for each $\phi \in F$, π'_ϕ denoting the canonical projection of C^F onto the component space C correlated with the index ϕ.

As C is dually universal for $K^o(C)$ (cf. section 1.6), there exists a continuous map ν of C onto X. This map induces a continuous map $\bar{\nu}$ of C^F onto X^F, where $\bar{\nu} \circ \pi_\phi = \pi'_\phi \circ \nu$, for all $\phi \in F$. Let $Y = (X\mu)\bar{\nu}^{-1}$; Y is a zero-dimensional compact metrizable space, the map $\tau = (\bar{\nu}|Y) \circ \mu^{-1} = (\bar{\nu}|Y) \circ \pi_{1_X}$ is a continuous map of Y onto X, and

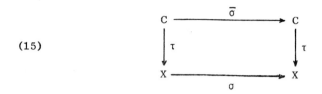

$\tau \circ \phi = (\phi^{+}|Y) \circ \tau$, for every $\phi \in F$.

Thus we have succeeded in lifting all $\phi \in F$, i.e. theorem 3.4.18 is now proved. Now let $F^{*} = \{\phi^{*}|X\mu : \phi \in F\}$ and $F^{+} = \{\phi^{+}|Y : \phi \in F\}$, both groups furnished with the topology of uniform convergence. Clearly the map $h : \phi^{+}|Y \to \phi^{*}|X\mu$ $(\phi \in F)$ is an isomorphism of F^{+} onto F^{*}; we must show that this map is continuous.

(17) 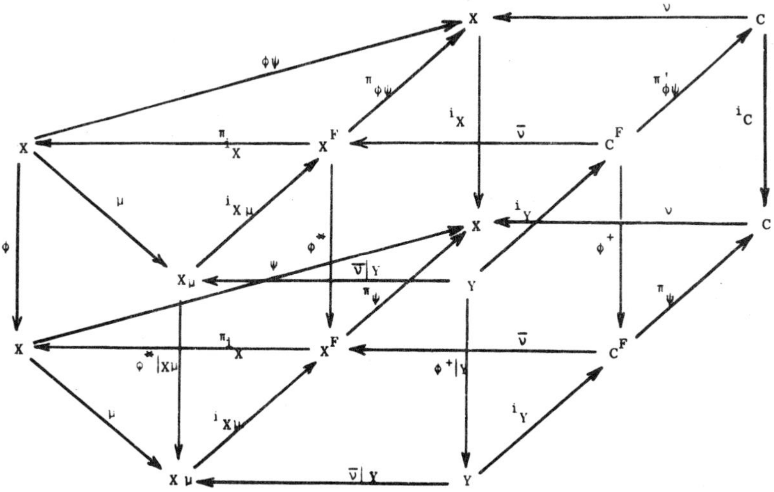

A basic neighbourhood of the identity element of F^{*} is of the form

(18) $$U = \{\phi^{*}|X\mu : (x, x\phi^{*}) \in W \text{ for all } x \in X\mu\},$$

where W is a neighbourhood of the diagonal in $X\mu \times X\mu$. It is to be shown that Uh^{-1} is a neighbourhood of i_Y in F^{+}. This is indeed the case: for Uh^{-1} contains the open subset

(19) $$V = \{\phi^{+}|Y : (y, y\phi^{+}) \in W' \text{ for all } y \in Y\}$$

of F^{+}, where W' is the following neighbourhood of the diagonal in $Y \times Y$:

(20) $$W' = \{(y_1, y_2) \in Y \times Y : (y_1\bar{\nu}, y_2\bar{\nu}) \in W\} = (W)(\bar{\nu} \times \bar{\nu})^{-1}.$$

(The fact that W' is a neighbourhood of the diagonal - W' is even open in $Y \times Y$! - is a consequence of the continuity of $\bar{\nu}$).

REMARK 5. It follows from the proof that in the raising procedure just described algebraic relations are again retained.

In particular:

3.4.20. COROLLARY. Every retraction of a compact metrizable space X can be raised to a retraction of the Cantor discontinuum C.

From theorem 3.4.19 in conjunction with corollary 3.4.14 we obtain at once the following slightly strengthened version of a result of J. DE GROOT and R.H. MCDOWELL [51] on metrizable groups:

3.4.21. THEOREM. Every countable metrizable group G is a continuous isomorphic image of a group of automorphisms of C, the last group furnished with the topology of uniform convergence.

Let K be the category of all uniformly continuous maps of one uniform space into another. In K, direct joins always exist: if X_t is a uniform space, for each $t \in T$, let $X = \prod_{t \in T} X_t$, furnished with the product uniformity, and for each $t \in T$ let $\pi_t : X \to X_t$ be the corresponding canonical projection: $(\xi_s)_{s \in T} \pi_t = \xi_t$. Then $(\pi_t)_{t \in T}$ is a direct join of $(X_t)_{t \in T}$.

By proposition 1.6.8, K admits a K^θ-universal object, for each $\theta \in$ ORD. Hence K contains K^θ-universal morphisms etc. As proposition 1.6.8 asserts that a "uniformly" K^θ-universal object exists, we even obtain, by arguments similar to those leading to theorem 3.3.4:

3.4.22. PROPOSITION. Let $\theta \in$ ORD. There exists a uniform space X, a uniformly continuous map $\Phi : X \to X$ and a uniform isomorphism Ψ of X onto itself for which the following is true. If U is an arbitrary uniform space of weight at most $\aleph_\theta$, and if $\phi : U \to U$ is uniformly continuous (if ψ is a uniform isomorphism of U onto itself), there exists a uniform isomorphism τ of U into X such that $\tau\Phi = \phi\tau$ (such that $\tau\Psi = \psi\tau$, respectively).

We conclude this section with an analogous result for metric spaces.

3.4.23. PROPOSITION. Let $\theta \in$ ORD. There exists a metric space X, a contraction $\Phi : X \to X$ and an isometry Ψ of X onto itself with the following properties. If M is any metric space of weight at most $\aleph_\theta$, and if $\phi : M \to M$ is a contraction (if ψ is an isometry of M onto itself), there exists an isometry $\tau : M \to X$ such that $\tau\Phi = \phi\tau$ (such that $\tau\Psi = \psi\tau$, respectively).

PROOF. As we do not know whether direct joins always exist in the category of all contracting maps of one metric space into another, a direct proof is presented. We restrict ourselves to the case of isometries.

Let Y be a metric space in which every metric space M of weight at most $\aleph_\theta$ can be isometrically embedded; such a space exists, according to proposition 1.6.7. We will denote the metric in Y, and in all other metric spaces occurring in this proof, by $|\,,\,|$.

Let X be the subset of Y^I, consisting of all bounded functions $I \to Y$; if $x = (\xi_k)_{k\in I} \in X$ and $y = (\eta_k)_{k\in I} \in X$, we define

(21) $$|x,y| = \sup_{k\in I} |\xi_k,\eta_k| .$$

This is a metric for X. Furthermore, we define $\Psi : X \to X$ through the conditions

(22) $$\Psi \circ \pi_k = \pi_{k+1},$$

for each $k \in I$, where π_k stands for the map $(\xi_h)_{h\in I} \to \xi_k$. Clearly Ψ is an isometry of X onto itself.

Now let M be an arbitrary metric space of weight at most $\aleph_\theta$, and let $\psi : M \to M$ be an isometry. Let μ be an isometric embedding of M into Y. We define a map $\tau : M \to X$ by the condition that

(23) $$\tau \circ \pi_k = \psi^k \circ \mu ,$$

for arbitrary $k \in I$. Then τ is an isometry, and $\tau \circ \Psi = \psi \circ \tau$.

3.5. Linearization of continuous self-maps

This section contains nothing essentially new. Rather, it is a connecting link between this chapter and the next one, showing how the problem of linearization of mappings is closely related to our considerations concerning universal continuous self-maps.

3.5.1. DEFINITION. Let E be a topological linear space. We say that a continuous self-map ϕ of a topological space X can be linearized in E if there exist a topological map τ : $X \to E$ and a continuous linear operator $\Phi : E \to E$ such that $\tau \circ \Phi = \phi \circ \tau$.

If ϕ can be linearized in E by means of the embedding τ, then clearly the subset $X\tau$ of E is invariant under the linearizing operator Φ, and $\phi = \tau \circ (\Phi|X\tau) \circ \tau^{-1}$.

3.5.2. DEFINITION. Let E be a topological vector space. If X is a topological space and F a semigroup of continuous self-maps of X, then an F-linearization of X is a topological map $\tau : X \to E$ with the following property: there exists an isomorphism h of the semigroup F into the semigroup of all continuous linear operators in E such that $\tau \circ (\phi h) = \phi \circ \tau$, for every $\phi \in F$.

(1)
$$\begin{array}{ccc} E & \xrightarrow{\ \phi h\ } & E \\ \uparrow \tau & & \uparrow \tau \\ X & \xrightarrow{\ \phi\ } & X \end{array}$$

REMARK 1. An F-linearization could be considered as an F-equivariant embedding in the sense of A. HELLER [57] .

A Tychonov cube $X = [0,1]^{\aleph_\theta}$ is a subspace of the space $E = R^{\aleph_\theta}$, R denoting the real line. If F is a semigroup, $\phi_o \in F$, and if $\phi_o^* : X^F \to X^F$ is again defined by

(2)
$$((x_\phi)_{\phi \in F})\phi_o^* = (x_{\phi_o\phi})_{\phi \in F},$$

for all points $(x_\phi)_{\phi \in F} \in X^F$, then ϕ_o^* is the restriction to X^F of the map $\hat{\phi}_o : E^F \to E^F$ such that

(3)
$$((x_\phi)_{\phi \in F})\hat{\phi}_o = (x_{\phi_o\phi})_{\phi \in F}$$

for all $(x_\phi)_{\phi \in F} \in E^F$. If we consider E^F as a topological linear space over R in the natural way (i.e. we consider E^F as a topological direct product of $\aleph_\theta$.card(F) linear spaces R), then each $\hat{\phi}_o$, $\phi_o \in F$, obviously is a continuous linear operator in E^F. Thus we find (cf. theorems 2.5.13 and 3.3.2):

3.5.3. PROPOSITION. Let $\theta \in$ ORD. There exists a topologically $(\aleph_\theta)$-universal semigroup S of morphisms (group G of bimorphisms) in K^θ(CR), consisting entirely of continuous linear operators in a topological vector space.

In particular, if S is a set of continuous self-maps of a completely regular space X, all maps of S can be simultaneously linearized in a (locally convex) linear space E of weight card(S).weight(X). .$\aleph_o$.

3.5.4. COROLLARY. For each $\theta \in$ ORD, there exists a continuous linear operator (a linear autohomeomorphism) in a complete locally convex linear space E of weight $\aleph_\theta$ which universally linearizes all continuous self-maps (all autohomeomorphisms, respectively) of completely regular spaces of weight at most $\aleph_\theta$.

If we are not interested in a universal linearization, we may replace the free group or semigroup figuring in the proofs of theorems 2.4.1 and 3.3.2 by the given group of autohomeomorphisms or semigroup of continuous self-maps. In this way we obtain:

3.5.5. PROPOSITION. Let F be a semigroup of continuous self-maps of a completely regular space X. Then there exists an F-linearization of X in the topological vector space R^κ with κ = card(F). .weight(X). $\aleph_o$.

If a continuous self-map $\phi : X \to X$ admits linearization in some topological linear space, then the space X is of necessity completely regular: every topological group, and a fortiori every topological vector space, is completely regular.

The results of this section show that conversely continuous self-maps of completely regular spaces always can be linearized,and even in topological linear spaces which are locally convex and complete and which have several other nice properties.

If one is interested in self-maps of metrizable spaces, these results are no longer satisfactory. For every metrizable space can be topologically embedded in some Hilbert space, and Hilbert spaces are much nicer generalizations, to infinite dimensions, of the finite-dimensional euclidean spaces R^n then are the spaces $R^{\aleph_\theta}$.

However, the methods of sections 2.4 and 3.3 can not be applied to Hilbert spaces, at least not without modifications: we have shown (corollary 3.2.12) that, in $K^\theta(H)$,

(4) $$\Delta(H, \aleph_\theta) = \emptyset$$

for each $\theta \in$ ORD and for each Hilbert space H containing more than one point.

It will be shown in chapter 4 how the methods of section 2.4 can indeed be modified - under additional assumptions - to give results in Hilbert spaces. So, for instance, whereas corollary 3.5.4 asserts that there exists a continuous linear operator in a Fréchet-space which is universal for all continuous self-maps of separable metrizable spaces, it will be shown in section 4.3 that there exists even a bounded linear operator in a separable Hilbert space enjoying this property.

3.6. Notes

In the category of all T_1-spaces, topological mappings into have been characterized by H.-J. KOWALSKY [68] in the following manner.

If K is an arbitrary category, and if $\alpha, \beta \in K$, we write

(1) $$\alpha \downarrow \beta$$

if ${}^\alpha\varepsilon = {}^\beta\varepsilon$, while moreover $\beta\gamma_1 = \beta\gamma_2$ for all $\gamma_1, \gamma_2 \in K$ such that $\alpha\gamma_1 = \alpha\gamma_2$. The morphism $\mu \in K$ is called an injection if it is a monomorphism satisfying the condition: whenever $\mu \downarrow \alpha, \alpha \in K$, there exists a $\beta \in K$ such that $\alpha = \beta\mu$.

(2)

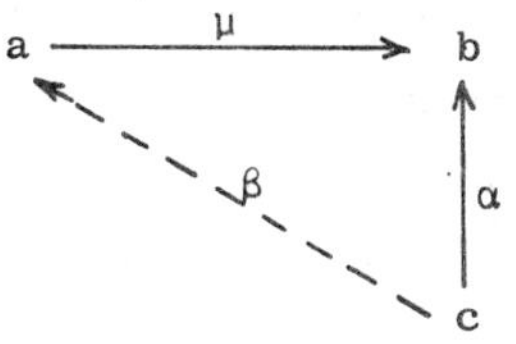

Now in the category of all T_1-spaces the injections turn out to be exactly the topological mappings into.

The same characterization is valid for the categories of topological spaces considered by us. As in most categories of algebraic systems every monomorphism is an injection, the considerations of chapter 3 and of chapter 4 could have been given a unified treatment by means of a change of the definitions of universal objects, morphisms, bimorphisms etc. requiring the existence of suitable injections instead of monomorphisms. We felt, however, that this would have been an unnatural complication in all non-topological cases.

H.-J. KOWALSKY calls a morphism ν of K which is an injection in the dual category K^* a <u>surjection</u>; in the category of all T_1-spaces (and also in the categories of topological spaces considered by us), the surjections are exactly the continuous maps ν of a space X onto a space Y such that Y has the quotient topology determined by ν . It can easily be verified that theorem 3.3.5 remains true if in the definitions of topologically dually universal objects, (bi-)morphisms, systems of morphisms etc. (definitions 3.1.1 and 3.1.2), the words "a surjection ν " are substituted for every occurrence of the words "a continuous map ν".

The results of section 3.3 are essentially contained in the preliminary note [8] .

The specific instances of proposition 3.4.4 embodied in corollaries 3.4.5 and 3.4.6 were suggested to us by J. DE GROOT.

Our definition of an S-compactification (definition 3.4.8) differs from the original one by J. DE GROOT and R.H. MCDOWELL [51] inasmuch we do not require the compactifying space X' to be metrizable. Theorem 3.4.10 is due to J. DE GROOT (oral communication); the special case expressed by corollary 3.4.11 was first proved by J. DE GROOT and

R.H. MCDOWELL [51] , using entirely different methods. Corollaries 3.4.12 and 3.4.15 are also proved in [51] , again in a completely different way.

As mentioned, the special case of theorem 3.4.18 obtained when only one mapping needs to be raised, is due to R.D. ANDERSON [4] . Our proof of theorem 3.4.18 (the first part of the proof of 3.4.19) is modelled after a proof of J. DE GROOT of this special case. This proof, which was orally communicated to us, differs considerably from R.D. ANDERSON's original proof.

Theorem 3.4.21 was proved by J. DE GROOT and R.H. MCDOWELL under the additional assumption that G is not discrete ([51] , corollary 2.9).

The results of section 3.5 are all due to J. DE GROOT [47,49] .

4. LINEARIZATION IN HILBERT SPACE

4.1. Discussion of the methods to be used

The methods of the previous chapters can be adapted in order to obtain results on linearization in Hilbert space of certain topological transformation groups acting on a metrizable space. In this preliminary sections it is explained why modifications are necessary, and a motivation is given for the methods that will be used.

In $K^{\theta}(H)$ every direct join is equivalent to a topological direct product; on the other hand, the direct product of more than finitely many non-trivial Hilbert spaces is not itself a Hilbert space (cf. proposition 3.2.12 and corollary 3.2.13). Therefore the methods of the previous two chapters do not work unmodified for Hilbert spaces.

One could try to replace direct products by Hilbert sums. We recall that the Hilbert sum of an arbitrary family $(H_t)_{t \in T}$ of Hilbert spaces (T a non-void index set) is the linear subspace

(1) $$\bigoplus_{t \in T} H_t = \{(x_t)_{t \in T} \in \mathbb{P}_{t \in T} H_t : \sum_{t \in T} \|x_t\|^2_{H_t} < \infty\}$$

of $\mathbb{P}_{t \in T} H_t$, with the inner product of $x = (x_t)_{t \in T}$ and $y = (y_t)_{t \in T}$ defined by

(2) $$(x,y) = \sum_{t \in T} (x_t, y_t).$$

If T is finite, then $\bigoplus_{t \in T} H_t = \mathbb{P}_{t \in T} H_t$; and $\bigoplus_{t \in T} H_t$ is a Hilbert space under all circumstances.

However, this replacement is inadequate. If e.g. S is an uncountable semigroup acting on a Hilbert space H, and if we would try to linearize the action of S by our standard construction, embedding H in $K = \bigoplus_{\sigma \in S} H$ by means of the map τ which sends $\xi \in H$ onto its orbit under S,

(3) $$\xi\tau = (\xi\sigma)_{\sigma \in S},$$

then, among other things, we must have $\xi\sigma = 0$ for all but countably many $\sigma \in S$. This imposes an extremely rigorous condition on the action of S.

We therefore propose to use a kind of "Hilbert integral" instead of Hilbert sums. We admit as index sets only groups or semigroups on which a suitable integral is defined (this practically limits us to locally compact groups). Given such a group or semigroup G and also a Hilbert space H, we will consider the linear space C(G,H) of all square-summable continuous maps $G \to H$, made into a prehilbert space in a natural way. More exactly, we define (limiting us, for the moment, to the case where G is a locally compact group):

4.1.1. DEFINITION. Let G be a locally compact group, and let H be a Hilbert space. Then C(G,H) denotes the linear space of all continuous maps $G \to H$ which are square-summable with respect to Haar measure in G. If $x,y \in C(G,H)$, we put

$$(x,y) = \int_G (x_\gamma, y_\gamma)\, d\gamma \ , \tag{4}$$

where x_γ (y_γ) stands for the value of the function x (of y, respectively) in $\gamma \in G$, and where $d\gamma$ denotes, as usual, the Haar measure in G.

It is immediately verified that by (4) an inner product is defined in C(G,H); in other words, C(G,H) is a prehilbert space.

The Hilbert sum of a number of copies of a Hilbert space H can be considered as a special case of the "Hilbert integral" C(G,H):

4.1.2. PROPOSITION. If G is a discrete group, and if the Haar measure on G is normed in such a way that every one-point set has measure 1, then

$$C(G,H) = \bigoplus_{\gamma \in G} H_\gamma \ , \tag{5}$$

where each H_γ coincides with H.

4.1.3. CONVENTIONS. In the sequel, we suppose the following conditions satisfied:

(i) The Haar measure on a locally compact group G is defined in such a way that it is left-invariant.

(ii) If G is compact, the Haar measure is normed in such a way that G has norm 1.

(iii) If G is discrete, the Haar measure is normed in such a way that every one-point set has measure 1.

Suppose now that G is a locally compact transformation group, acting on a metrizable space X. Then X can be embedded as a bounded set in a Hilbert space H (proposition 1.4.8); let us suppose that X is already a subspace of the unit ball of H. What can we say now about the map τ, sending each $x \in X$ onto its G-orbit?

If we put $x\tau = \xi$, where ξ is the function $G \to H$ such that

(6) $$(\gamma)\xi = (x)\gamma$$

for every $\gamma \in G$ (in complete accordance with (3)), then ξ certainly is a continuous function, but ξ need not be an element of $C(G,H)$: ξ need not be square-summable!

It is in order to remedy this defect that we in the next section introduce weight functions. Such a weight function f (there need not always exist one, probably) correlates a scalar to every $\gamma \in G$ in such a way that for every $x \in X$ the map $\xi: G \to H$, defined by

(7) $$(\gamma)\xi = (\gamma f)\cdot(x\gamma),$$

for all $\gamma \in G$, is an element of $C(G,H)$. Moreover, the definition of a weight function is carefully tailored to ensure that the mapping $\tau : X \to C(G,H)$, sending $x \in X$ onto the $\xi \in C(G,H)$ defined by (7), is a topological embedding, and that for every $\gamma \in G$ a bounded linear operator $\gamma^* : C(G,H) \to C(G,H)$ can be defined such that $\tau \circ \gamma^* = \gamma \circ \tau$. In effect, the homeomorphism

(8) $$\tau : X \to X\tau \subset C(G,H) \subset H^G$$

turns out to be such that on $X\tau$ the topology determined by the prehilbert norm coincides with the weak topology, i.e. the topology induced by the product topology of H^G, and the map γ^* is essentially a "permutation of the axes" of H^G, of the same type considered already so often in the previous chapters.

4.2. Weight functions and W-groups

In this section we define weight functions, and we prove that such functions exist for a large class of groups. This class contains all compact groups, all countable discrete groups, the additive group of real numbers; moreover it is closed under finite direct products and under group extensions of a certain type, and each subgroup of a group in the class itself belongs to it. It follows that a locally compact abelian group admits a weight if it is either separable or compactly generated.

4.2.1. DEFINITION. Let G be a locally compact group. A weight function or weight on G is a continuous real-valued function f on G with the following properties:

(i) $(\varepsilon)f = 1$ (ε = unit of G); $(\gamma)f > 0$ for every $\gamma \in G$;

(ii) $(\gamma_1\gamma_2)f \geq (\gamma_1)f\cdot(\gamma_2)f$, for arbitrary $\gamma_1, \gamma_2 \in G$;

(iii) f is square-summable with respect to Haar measure in G.

A locally compact group G is called a W-group if there exists a weight on G.

4.2.2. LEMMA. Let G be a locally compact group, and let f be a weight on G. Then there exists a sequence of compact subsets C_n of G such that

(1) $$\lim_{n\to\infty}\int_{G\setminus C_n}(\gamma f)^2 d\gamma = 0.$$

PROOF. As f^2 is a non-negative measurable function such that $\int_G (\gamma f)^2 d\gamma < \infty$ (condition (iii) of definition 4.2.1), there exists a function g defined on G such that

(2) $$0 \leq (\gamma)g \leq (\gamma f)^2, \text{ for all } \gamma \in G;$$

(3) $$\int_G (\gamma)g\, d\gamma = \int_G (\gamma f)^2 d\gamma ;$$

while moreover for each real $\alpha \geq 0$ the set

(4) $$\{\gamma \in G : (\gamma)g > \alpha\}$$

is σ-compact (cf. [58] , theorem 11.40). Let $A = \{\gamma \in G : (\gamma)g > 0\}$.
Then

(5) $$\int_G (\gamma f)^2 d\gamma \geq \int_A (\gamma f)^2 d\gamma \geq \int_A (\gamma)g \, d\gamma = \int_G (\gamma)g \, d\gamma = $$
$$= \int_G (\gamma f)^2 d\gamma ;$$

hence

(6) $$\int_G (\gamma f)^2 d\gamma = \int_A (\gamma f)^2 d\gamma .$$

As A is σ-compact, there are compact subsets $C_o, C_1, C_2, \ldots$ of G such that $C_n \subset C_{n+1}$ for all $n \in N$ while moreover $A = \bigcup_{n \in N} C_n$. It follows that

(7) $$\int_G (\gamma f)^2 d\gamma = \lim_{n \to \infty} \int_{C_n} (\gamma f)^2 d\gamma$$

which is equivalent to the assertion (1).

4.2.3. PROPOSITION. Every countable discrete group is a W-group.

PROOF. I. First we consider a free group F with denumerably many free generators α_n, $n \in N \setminus \{0\}$. Let ε be the unit of F.

Every $\phi \in F, \phi \neq \varepsilon$, can be uniquely written as a reduced word

(8) $$\phi = \alpha_{n_1}^{k_1} \alpha_{n_2}^{k_2} \ldots \alpha_{n_s}^{k_s} ;$$

we put

(9) $$(\phi)f = 2^{-\sum_{\sigma=1}^{s} |k_\sigma| \cdot n_\sigma}$$

and

(10) $$(\varepsilon)f = 1.$$

If ϕ is the reduced word (8), the <u>length</u> of ϕ is the integer $\sum_{\sigma=1}^{s} |k_\sigma|$. By induction on the length of ϕ, one easily shows that, for each $n \in N$,

(11) $$\Sigma \{ (\phi f)^2 : \phi \in F \text{ and length}(\phi)=n\} \leq (\tfrac{2}{3})^n ;$$

hence

(12) $$\sum_{\phi \in F} (\phi f)^2 < \infty .$$

Thus in order to show that f is a weight on F it only remains to prove that condition (ii) of definition 4.2.1 is satisfied.

Let $\phi_1, \phi_2 \in F$, and first suppose that ϕ_2 has length 1. Then ϕ_2 is of the form α_n^i, $i = \pm 1$. If $\phi_1 = \varepsilon$, we have

(13) $$(\phi_1\phi_2)f = \phi_2 f = (\phi_1 f)\cdot(\phi_2 f).$$

If ϕ_1 has (8) as its reduced form, then

(14) $$(\phi_1\phi_2)f = \begin{cases} 2^n \cdot \phi_1 f & \text{if } k_s = n \text{ and } i\cdot k_s < 0; \\ 2^{-n}\cdot \phi_1 f & \text{otherwise.} \end{cases}$$

Hence $(\phi_1\phi_2)f \geq 2^{-n}\cdot\phi_1 f = (\phi_1 f)\cdot(\phi_2 f)$ in all cases.

Using induction on the length of ϕ_2, one can now easily show that $(\phi_1\phi_2)f \geq (\phi_1 f)\cdot(\phi_2 f)$ for arbitrary $\phi_1, \phi_2 \in F$.

II. Now let G be an arbitrary countable group. Then there exists a homomorphism h of F onto G. We define, for $\gamma \in G$:

(15) $$\gamma f_o = \sup \{\phi f : \phi \in \gamma h^{-1}\} .$$

It follows from the way in which f was defined that not only this supremum exists as a finite number, but that even

(16) $$\gamma f_o = \max \{\phi f : \phi \in \gamma h^{-1}\} .$$

Hence if $\gamma_1, \gamma_2 \in G$, there are $\phi_1, \varphi_2 \in F$ such that

(17) $$\phi_i h = \gamma_i \quad ; \quad \phi_i f = \gamma_i f_o \qquad (i=1,2);$$

It follows that

(18) $$(\gamma_1\gamma_2)f_o \geq (\phi_1\phi_2)f \geq (\phi_1 f)\cdot(\phi_2 f) = (\gamma_1 f_o)\cdot(\gamma_2 f_o).$$

Moreover,

(19) $$\sum_{\gamma \in G} (\gamma f_o)^2 \leq \sum_{\phi \in F} (\phi f)^2 < \infty .$$

Thus f_o is a weight for G.

4.2.4. THEOREM. Every compact group is a W-group.

PROOF. If G is compact, the function which is identically 1 on G is a weight.

4.2.5. PROPOSITION. Let G be a locally compact group, and suppose G contains a compact normal subgroup G_o such that the factor group G/G_o is discrete and countable. Then G is a W-group.

PROOF. Let f_o be a weight for G/G_o. We define, for $\gamma \in G$:

$$\gamma f = (\gamma G_o) f_o . \tag{20}$$

Then f satisfies condition (i) of definition 4.1.1; and, for arbitrary $\gamma_1, \gamma_2 \in G$:

$$\begin{aligned}(\gamma_1\gamma_2)f &= (\gamma_1\gamma_2 G_o)f_o = (\gamma_1 G_o \cdot \gamma_2 G_o)f_o \geq \\ &\geq (\gamma_1 G_o)f_o \cdot (\gamma_2 G_o)f_o = (\gamma_1 f)\cdot(\gamma_2 f).\end{aligned} \tag{21}$$

As f is constant on cosets and as every coset is open, f is continuous. Moreover, the distinct cosets partition G in countably many measurable sets of finite measure; if we normalize Haar measure on G such that all these cosets have measure 1, we find

$$\begin{aligned}\int_G (\gamma f)^2 d\gamma &= \sum_{A \in G/G_o} \int_A (\gamma f)^2 d\gamma = \\ &= \sum_{A \in G/G_o} (Af_o)^2 < \infty .\end{aligned} \tag{22}$$

4.2.6. PROPOSITION. The additive group R of all real numbers, with the usual topology, is a W-group.

PROOF. The function $x \to e^{-|x|}$, $x \in R$, is a weight on R.

4.2.7. PROPOSITION. Every subgroup of a W-group is a W-group.

PROOF: evident.

4.2.8. PROPOSITION. Every finite product $G_1 \times G_2 \times \ldots \times G_n$ of W-groups $G_1, G_2, \ldots, G_n$ is again a W-group.

PROOF. Let f_k be a weight on G_k, $k=1,2,\ldots,n$. We define f on the product group as follows:

(23) $$(\gamma_1,\gamma_2,\ldots,\gamma_n)f = (\gamma_1 f_1)\cdot(\gamma_2 f_2)\ \ldots\ (\gamma_n f_n).$$

Then f is a weight (condition (iii) follows from FUBINI's theorem; the other conditions are evidently satisfied).

4.2.9. THEOREM. Every separable locally compact abelian group is a W-group.

PROOF. Let G be a separable locally compact abelian group. Then G is topologically isomorphic to a direct product $R^n \times G'$, where G' contains a compact subgroup G_o such that G'/G_o is discrete (see A. WEIL [108] , p.110). As G is separable, G'/G_o must be countable. Now apply propositions 4.2.3, 4.2.5, 4.2.6 and 4.2.8.

4.2.10. THEOREM. Every locally compact compactly generated abelian group is a W-group.

PROOF. Let G be a locally compact compactly generated abelian group. Then G is topologically isomorphic to a direct product $R^n \times I^m \times G_o$, where $n,m \in N$, I is the additive group of all integers and G_o is a compact group (cf. e.g. [58] , theorem 9.8). Now use propositions 4.2.3, 4.2.4, 4.2.6 and 4.2.8.

4.2.11. DEFINITION. A topological group is called a CW-group if it is the image of a W-group under a continuous homomorphism.

4.3. Linearization of CW-groups

We will now prove that CW-transformation groups acting on metrizable spaces can be linearized in a Hilbert space. For compact transformation groups this is a result of J. DE GROOT (cf. [49]); his proof, presented in [50], served as a model for the proof of theorem 4.3.1 below.

4.3.1. THEOREM. Let G be a topological transformation group acting on a metrizable space M of weight $\aleph_\theta$. If G is a CW-group, then it can be linearized in a Hilbert space H of weight $\aleph_\theta$.

PROOF. Let h be a continuous homomorphism of a W-group F onto G; and let f be a weight function on F.

According to proposition 1.4.8 it is possible to embed M topologically into a Hilbert space H_o as a bounded set. To simplify our notation we suppose that M is given at the outset as a subset of the unit ball of H_o.

If $\xi \in M$, we define

(1) $$\xi\tau = x = (x_\phi)_{\phi \in F} \in H_o^F$$

where

(2) $$x_\phi = (\phi f)\cdot(\xi)(\phi h).$$

As f,h and ϕh are continuous, x is continuous on F. As f is square-summable, while

(3) $$\|(\xi)(\phi h)\| \leq 1$$

for all $\xi \in M$ and all $\phi \in F$, x is a square-summable function. Hence τ is a map of M into $C(F,H_o)$.

The map τ is 1-1, for if ε denotes the unit element of F, then

(4) $$(\xi\tau)_\varepsilon = (\varepsilon f)\cdot(\xi)(\varepsilon h) = \xi;$$

we will show that τ is topological.

First we prove that τ is continuous. Take any $x \in M_\tau$, say $x = \xi\tau$, and an arbitrary $\delta > 0$. If $y \in M\tau$, say $y = \eta\tau$, then

(5) $$\|x-y\|^2 = \int_F (\phi f)^2 \cdot \|(\xi)(\phi h)-(\eta)(\phi h)\|^2 d\phi$$

Let $\{F_n\}_{n \in N}$ be a sequence of compact subsets of F such that

(6) $$\lim_{n\to\infty} \int_{F \setminus F_n} (\phi f)^2 d\phi = 0$$

(cf. lemma 4.2.2) and let $n_o \in N$ such that

$$(7) \qquad \int_{F\setminus F_{n_o}} (\phi f)^2 d\phi < \frac{\delta^2}{16} .$$

Then we have (using (3)):

$$(8) \qquad ||x-y||^2 \leq \int_{F_{n_o}} (\phi f)^2 \cdot ||(\xi)(\phi h)-(\eta)(\phi h)||^2 d\phi + \frac{\delta^2}{4} .$$

For each $\phi \in F$ there exists a neighbourhood U_ϕ of ϕh in G and a neighbourhood V_ϕ of ξ in M such that

$$(9) \qquad ||(\xi)(\phi h)-\eta\gamma|| < \frac{\delta}{8} \cdot (\int_F (\phi f)^2 d\phi)^{-\frac{1}{2}}$$

for all $\gamma \in U_\phi$ and all $\eta \in V_\phi$. It follows that, for $\gamma \in U_\phi$ and $\eta \in V_\phi$,

$$(10) \qquad \begin{aligned} ||\xi\gamma-\eta\gamma|| &\leq ||(\xi)(\phi h) -\xi\gamma|| + ||(\xi)(\phi h)-\eta\gamma|| < \\ &< \delta\ (4 \int_F (\phi f)^2 d\phi)^{-\frac{1}{2}}. \end{aligned}$$

The compact set F_{n_o} may be covered by finitely many of the sets $U_\phi h^{-1}$, say by $U_{\phi_1} h^{-1}$, $U_{\phi_2} h^{-1}, \dots, U_{\phi_n} h^{-1}$. Put $V = V_{\phi_1} \cap V_{\phi_2} \cap \dots \cap V_{\phi_n}$; then

$$(11) \qquad ||(\xi)(\phi h)-(\eta)(\phi h)|| < \delta \cdot (4 \int_F (\phi f)^2 d\phi)^{-\frac{1}{2}}$$

for all $\phi \in F$ and all $\eta \in V$, and hence

$$(12) \qquad \int_{F_{n_o}} (\phi f)^2 \cdot ||(\xi)(\phi h)-(\eta)(\phi h)||^2 d\phi < \frac{\delta^2}{4}$$

for every $\eta \in V$. Combining this with (8), we obtain that $||x-y|| < \delta$ as soon as $\eta \in V$, and it follows that τ is continuous.

Next we show that τ^{-1} is continuous. Suppose this were not the case at the point $x = \xi\tau$. Then there must exist a sequence of points $\eta_n \in M$ and a $\delta > 0$ such that for all n

$$(13) \qquad ||\xi\tau - \eta_n\tau|| < \frac{1}{n} , ||\xi - \eta_n|| > \delta.$$

We assert that for each $\gamma \in G$ there exists a $\delta_\gamma > 0$ and a neighbourhood U_γ of γ in G such that

(14) $$\|\xi\chi - \eta_n\chi\| \geqq \delta_\gamma \quad \text{for all } \chi \in U_\gamma ,$$

for all but finitely many n.

Assuming for the moment the validity of this assertion, we proceed in the following manner. Let $n \in N$ such that $\int_{F_n} (\phi f)^2 d\phi \neq 0$. The compact set F_n may be covered by finitely many sets $U_\gamma h^{-1}$, say by $U_{\gamma_1} h^{-1}, U_{\gamma_2} h^{-1}, \ldots, U_{\gamma_n} h^{-1}$. Let $\delta_n = \min(\delta_{\gamma_1}, \ldots, \delta_{\gamma_n})$; then for almost all k we have that

(15) $$\|(\xi)(\phi h) - (\eta_k)(\phi h)\|^2 \geqq \delta_n \quad \text{for all } \phi \in F_n .$$

It follows that

(16) $$\frac{1}{k^2} > \|\xi\tau - \eta_k\tau\|^2 \geqq \int_{F_n} (\phi f)^2 \cdot \|(\xi)(\phi h) - (\eta_k)(\phi h)\|^2 d\phi \geqq$$
$$\geqq \delta_n^2 \cdot \int_{F_n} (\phi f)^2 d\phi$$

for almost all k, which is absurd.

It remains to prove the assertion. Assume it were false. Then for some $\gamma_o \in G$ there would exist a sequence $\gamma_n \to \gamma_o$ such that, for each n,

(17) $$\|\xi\gamma_n - \eta_k \gamma_n\| < \frac{1}{n}$$

for infinitely many η_k. Select a subsequence $\{\eta_{k_n}\}_{n \in N}$ of $\{\eta_k\}_{k \in N}$ such that

(18) $$\|\xi\gamma_n - \eta_{k_n} \gamma_n\| < \frac{1}{n}$$

for all n. As $\xi\gamma_n \to \xi\gamma_o$, it follows that $\eta_{k_n}\gamma_n \to \xi\gamma_o$; but $\gamma_n \to \gamma_o$ implies that $\gamma_n^{-1} \to \gamma_o^{-1}$, and we find that

(19) $$\eta_{k_n} \to \xi,$$

contradicting (13).

Thus τ is indeed a topological embedding of M into $C(F, H_o)$. We shall now exhibit the linear operators in $C(F, H_o)$ by which the $\gamma \in G$ are linearized.

If $\phi_o \in F$ and $x \in C(F,H_o)$, we put

(20) $$x\vec{\phi_o} = y = (y_\phi)_{\phi \in F}$$

with

(21) $$y_\phi = \frac{\phi f}{(\phi_o \phi) f} \cdot x_{\phi_o \phi} \;.$$

It follows from condition (ii) of definition 4.2.1 that

(22) $$\|x\vec{\phi_o}\| \leqq (\phi_o f)^{-1} \cdot \|x\| \;;$$

hence $\vec{\phi_o}$ is a bounded linear operator in $C(F,H_o)$, with norm

(23) $$\|\vec{\phi_o}\| \leqq (\phi_o f)^{-1}.$$

One verifies at once that

(24) $$\overrightarrow{\phi_1 \phi_2} = \vec{\phi_1} \cdot \vec{\phi_2};$$

hence every $\vec{\phi}$ is invertible, and the transformation $\phi \to \vec{\phi}$ is a homomorphism of F onto a group $\vec{F}$ of invertible bounded linear operators in $C(F,H_o)$ (in fact, it is even an isomorphism).

We now show that

(25) $$\vec{\phi}|M\tau = \tau^{-1} \circ \phi h \circ \tau$$

for arbitrary $\phi \in F$. In fact, let $x \in M\tau$, say $x = \xi\tau$. Then

$$(x\vec{\phi})_\psi = (\xi\tau\vec{\phi})_\psi = \frac{\psi f}{(\phi\psi) f} \cdot (\xi\tau)_{\phi\psi} =$$

(26) $$= \frac{\psi f}{(\phi\psi) f} \cdot (\phi\psi) f \cdot (\xi)((\phi\psi)h) =$$

$$= \psi f \cdot ((\xi)(\phi h))(\psi h) =$$

$$= ((\xi(\phi h))\tau)_\psi = (x\tau^{-1}(\phi h)\tau)_\psi \;,$$

for every $\psi \in F$. Hence (G,M) and $(\vec{F}|M\tau, M\tau)$ are equivalent.

Let K be the linear subspace of $C(F,H_o)$ spanned by $M\tau$; as $M\tau$ is invariant under $\vec{F}$ (by (25)), so is K. Let H be any completion of K;

all invertible bounded linear operators $\vec{\phi}|K$ can be uniquely extended to invertible bounded linear operators ϕ^* in H. As the weight of H is at most $\aleph_0 \cdot$ weight(M), this completes the proof.

REMARK 1. We announced in section 4.1 that the embedding τ of M into $C(F,H_o)$ would be such that the topology $\mathcal{T}_1$ induced in $M\tau$ by $C(F,H_o)$ coincides with the weak topology $\mathcal{T}_2$.

This is indeed the case. The fact that $\mathcal{T}_1 \subset \mathcal{T}_2$ follows from the continuity of τ: $\|x-y\| < \varepsilon$ as soon as y_ε belongs to a small enough neighbourhood of x_ε (cf.(4)). The fact that $\mathcal{T}_2 \subset \mathcal{T}_1$ is implied by the continuity of τ^{-1}; for the continuity of τ^{-1} is equivalent to the continuity of the projection map $\pi_\varepsilon|M\tau$, sending x onto x_ε; as

(27) $$x_\phi = (\phi f)\cdot(x_\varepsilon)(\phi h),$$

and as each $\phi h : M \to M$ $(\phi \in F)$ is continuous, it follows that $\pi_\phi|M\tau$ is continuous for all $\phi \in F$. And the product topology in H_o^F is exactly the weakest topology for which all $\pi_\phi, \phi \in F$, are continuous.

If G is a W-group, we can take F = G in the proof of theorem 4.3.1. As the group $G^* = \{\gamma^* : \gamma \in G\}$ is isomorphic to $\vec{G} = \{\vec{\gamma} : \gamma \in G\}$, and as this last group is isomorphic to G, we have:

4.3.2. COROLLARY. Let G be a topological transformation group acting on a metrizable space M of weight at most $\aleph_\theta$. If G is a W-group, there exists a G-linearization (cf. definition 3.5.2) of M in a Hilbert space H of weight $\aleph_\theta$.

4.3.3. COROLLARY. Let G be a compact transformation group acting on a metrizable space M of weight at most $\aleph_\theta$. Then there exists a G-linearization of M into a Hilbert space H of weight $\aleph_\theta$ such that the action of G is linearized by a group G^* of unitary operators in H.

PROOF. In the proof of theorem 4.3.1 we take F = G; for f we take the function which is identically 1 on G. It then follows from (20) and (21) (and from the left invariance of Haar measure) that every operator $\vec{\phi}_o$ is unitary, and hence also every ϕ^*.

4.3.4. COROLLARY. Let G be an abelian locally compact transformation group acting on a metrizable space M, and suppose G is either separable or compactly generated. Then there exists a G-linearization of M in a Hilbert space H of weight $\aleph_0 \cdot$ weight(M).

PROOF. This follows from corollary 4.3.2 and theorems 4.2.9 and 4.2.10.

4.3.5. COROLLARY. If G is a countable transformation group acting on a metrizable space M of weight at most $\aleph_\theta$, there exists a G-linearization of M in a Hilbert space of weight $\aleph_\theta$.

PROOF. This follows from corollary 4.3.2 together with theorem 4.2.3.

The groups in corollary 4.3.5 need not be abelian. We do not know whether corollary 4.3.4 can be extended to cover also all non-commutative separable or compactly generated locally compact transformation groups.

REMARK 2. It follows from (23) that the linear operators $\phi^*: H \to H$, $\phi \in F$ (using the notation of the proof of theorem 4.3.1) satisfy the condition

(28) $$\|\phi^*\| \leqq (\phi f)^{-1}.$$

This suggests a relation between condition (ii) of definition 4.2.1 and the well-known norm-inequality $\|\alpha \circ \beta\| \leqq \|\alpha\| \cdot \|\beta\|$ for the composition of two bounded linear operators α, β. In fact, suppose G is a group of bounded linear operators in a Hilbert space H, topologized in such a way that it is a locally compact transformation group acting on H. Then the scalar function f on G, defined by

(29) $$(\gamma)f = \|\gamma\|^{-1}, \quad \gamma \in G,$$

is a lower semicontinuous function satisfying the first two conditions of definition 4.2.1. It would be interesting to know under which circumstances f is a weight function on G.

4.4. Linearization of transformation semigroups

In the preceding chapters transformation groups and transformation semigroups received parallel treatment: if results could be obtained for groups of bimorphisms, then also for semigroups of morphisms, and vice versa.

This parallelism no longer exists in our present considerations. This is a consequence of the fact that no really satisfactory analogue of the Haar integral is known for, say, locally compact semigroups.

Such results as can be obtained for transformation semigroups by means of the methods of the previous two sections, are discussed below.

Let us examine to what extent the proof of theorem 4.3.1 can be adapted to some class of topological transformation semigroups.

The existence of inverses in G (or rather F) was used twice. At one place we will certainly no longer need it, sc. where we used it in concluding from formula (24) in section 4.3 that every $\vec{\phi}$ is invertible (for of course when considering a transformation <u>semi</u>group we no longer strive for a linearization by <u>invertible</u> operators). More serious was the use made of inverses (particularly, of the continuity of taking inverses) in proving that the inverse τ^{-1} of the embedding map τ is continuous (the step from (18) to (19) in section 4.3).

We used extensively the existence of Haar measure in F. Close inspection of the proof reveals that the properties of Haar measure that were used are the following three:

(i) it is a non-negative regular Borel measure;

(ii) its support is the whole set F;

(iii) it is left sub-invariant, in the following (weak) sense: there exists a real constant $c > 0$ such that

$$(1) \qquad \int_F (\phi_o\phi)f\, d\phi \leqq c \int_F (\phi)f\, d\phi$$

for every non-negative real-valued continuous function f on F and for every $\phi_o \in F$.

4.4.1. DEFINITION. An IW-semigroup is a locally compact topological semigroup with unit F with the following properties:

(I) There exists a measure μ in F satisfying conditions (i)-(iii) above.

(II) There exists a real-valued function f on F satisfying conditions (i) - (iii) of definition 4.2.1 with respect to the integral defined by μ.

A topological semigroup with unit is called a CIW-semigroup if it is a continuous homomorphic image of an IW-semigroup.

4.4.2. PROPOSITION. Let G be a topological transformation semigroup acting on a compact metrizable space M. If G is a CIW-semigroup, then G can be linearized in a separable Hilbert space.

PROOF. The proof proceeds exactly as the proof of theorem 4.3.1 except that the continuity of τ^{-1} now is concluded from the compactness of M.

IW-semigroups seem to be exceedingly rare; we know of no extensive class except the rather trivial one consisting of all subsemigroups of W-groups. A less extensive class is the one consisting of all discrete countable cancellation semigroups with unit: the measure μ such that every one-point set has measure 1 satisfies the conditions (i)-(iii) above, and the existence of a weight function follows from

4.4.3. LEMMA. Let G be a countable semigroup, with neutral element ε. There exists a real-valued function f on G such that

(i) $\varepsilon f = 1$; $\gamma f > 0$ for all $\gamma \in G$;

(ii) $(\gamma_1\gamma_2)f \geqq (\gamma_1 f).(\gamma_2 f)$, for arbitrary $\gamma_1, \gamma_2 \in G$;

(iii) $\sum_{\gamma \in G} (\gamma f)^2 < \infty$.

PROOF. Similar to the proof of proposition 4.2.3.

More generally: if G is a countable discrete semigroup for which there exists a natural number n such that the set

$$\{\gamma \in G : (\exists \gamma_0 \in G)(\gamma_0\gamma = \gamma_1)\} \tag{2}$$

has at most n elements, for every choice of $\gamma_1 \in G$, then G is an IW-semigroup. In particular, every finite semigroup is an IW-semigroup.

As every free semigroup is a cancellation semigroup, every countable discrete semigroup is a CIW-semigroup. Thus every countable semigroup of continuous self-maps of a compact metrizable space can be linearized in separable Hilbert space.

More can be proved: in the case of a countable transformation semigroup G the hypothesis that the space X acted upon by G is compact, is superfluous:

4.4.4. PROPOSITION. Let G be a countable transformation semigroup acting continuously on a metrizable space M. Then the action of G can be linearized in a Hilbert space H of weight $\aleph_0 \cdot$weight(M).

PROOF. Let F be a free semigroup with unit with $\aleph_0$ generators. The proof of theorem 4.3.1 can easily be adapted to the discrete semigroup F, furnished with the measure μ such that every one-point subset of F has measure 1. The only part of the proof where difficulties arise is in showing that τ^{-1} is continuous. However, this is now almost evident: if $\xi, \eta \in M$, then

$$\|(\xi\tau)\tau^{-1} - (\eta\tau)\tau^{-1}\| = \|\xi - \eta\| \leqq$$

$$(3) \qquad \leqq \left(\sum_{\phi \in F} (\phi f)^2 \cdot \|(\xi)(\phi h) - (\eta)(\phi h)\|^2 \right)^{\frac{1}{2}} =$$

$$= \|\xi\tau - \eta\tau\| .$$

In particular, countably many continuous self-maps of a metrizable space M can be simultaneously linearized in a Hilbert space H of weight $\aleph_0 \cdot$ weight(M).

It is not known whether every compact semigroup is a CIW-semigroup (it seems highly improbable that this will be the case).

PROBLEM 2. To give a simple example of a compact transformation semigroup operating on a metrizable space which can not be linearized by a semigroup of bounded linear operators in some Hilbert space.

If the topological transformation semigroup S, acting on a metrizable space M, is an IW-semigroup, we see from proof 4.3.1 that there exists an S-linearization of M. We do not know whether every countable discrete semigroup is an IW-semigroup; therefore we also do not know whether proposition 4.4.4 can be strengthened to assert the existence of a G-linearization.

PROBLEM 3. Does there exist a G-linearization in a Hilbert space for every countable semigroup of continuous self-maps of a metrizable space?

4.5. Universal linearization

The considerations of the preceding two sections are used in this one in order to show that each category $K^{\theta}(M)$, $\theta \in$ ORD, contains universal morphisms and bimorphisms which are bounded linear operators in some Hilbert space. Some results in this direction are obtained also for systems of morphisms.

4.5.1. PROPOSITION. Let F be a W-group, and let H be a Hilbert space of weight $\aleph_\theta$, $\theta \in$ ORD. There exists a group F^* of bounded linear operators in H, isomorphic to the group F, with the following property. If X is any metrizable space of weight at most $\aleph_\theta$, and if G is a topological transformation group acting on X such that G is a continuous homomorphic image of F, then the pair (G,X) is topologically equivalent to a pair $(F^* | Y, Y)$ for a suitable F^*-invariant subspace Y of the topological space H.

PROOF. This follows at once from the proof of theorem 4.3.1.

4.5.2. COROLLARY. Let H be a Hilbert space of weight $\aleph_\theta$, $\theta \in$ ORD. There exists a group F of bounded linear operators in H which is a topologically $(\aleph_0)$-universal group of bimorphisms for the category $K^\theta(M)$.

One can say that the pair (F,H) universally linearizes all pairs (G,X) where X is a metrizable space of weight at most $\aleph_\theta$, and where G is a countable group of autohomeomorphisms of X.

4.5.3. COROLLARY. Let $\theta \in$ ORD, and let H be a Hilbert space of weight $\aleph_\theta$. There exists a linear autohomeomorphism Φ of H which is a topologically universal bimorphism for $K^\theta(M)$.

In other words, every autohomeomorphism ϕ of a metrizable space X of weight at most $\aleph_\theta$ can be linearized in H by means of Φ . For the case $\theta=0$ the existence of such a linear universal autohomeomorphism has been proved by A.H. COPELAND Jr. and J. DE GROOT ([18] , theorem I).

In order to prove corollary 4.5.3 one applies proposition 4.5.1, taking for F an infinite cyclic group, say the additive group I of all integers. If one uses the weight f on F defined by

$$(1) \qquad (k)f = 2^{-k},$$

the construction in proof 4.3.1 leads to the following explicit example of a linear universal autohomeomorphism Φ in $K^{\theta}(M)$.

Let H_0 be any Hilbert space of weight $\aleph_\theta$; for each $k \in I$, let $H_k = H_0$; and let

$$(2) \qquad H = \bigoplus_{k \in I} H_k .$$

If $x \in H$, say $x = (x_k)_{k \in I}$, we put

$$(3) \qquad x\Phi = y = (y_k)_{k \in I}$$

where

$$(4) \qquad y_k = \begin{cases} 2x_{k+1} & \text{if } k \geq 0; \\ \frac{1}{2}x_{k+1} & \text{if } k < 0. \end{cases}$$

Then Φ satisfies the requirements of corollary 4.5.3. (If $\theta=0$, this is exactly the operator constructed by A.H. COPELAND Jr. and J. DE GROOT [18] .)

*4.5.4. COROLLARY. Let $\theta, \kappa \in$ ORD, $0 < \kappa$. Let H be a Hilbert space of weight $\aleph_\theta$. There exists a group F of linear autohomeomorphisms of H with weight(F) $= \aleph_\kappa$, enjoying the following property. If X is any metrizable space of weight at most $\aleph_\theta$, and if G is any abelian compact transformation group, acting on X, of weight at most $\aleph_\kappa$, there exists an F-invariant subspace Y of the topological space H such that the pairs (G,X) and $(F|Y,Y)$ are topologically equivalent.

PROOF. According to corollary *1.4.13, $K(AG,\kappa)$ admits a universal object F_o. Let F_1 be the character group of the discrete group F_o. Then F_1 is a compact group of weight $\aleph_\kappa$ (cf. [58], theorem 24.14), and every compact abelian group G of weight at most $\aleph_\kappa$ is a continuous homomorphic image of F (cf. [58], proposition 24.41). As F_1 is a W-group (theorem 4.2.4), we need now only apply proposition 4.5.1.

From the results of section 4.4 we derive in the same way the following two propositions:

4.5.5. PROPOSITION. Let $\theta \in$ ORD, and let H be a Hilbert space of weight $\aleph_\theta$. There exists a semigroup S of bounded linear operators in H which is a topologically $(\aleph_o)$-universal semigroup of morphisms in $K^\theta(M)$.

4.5.6. PROPOSITION. Let $\theta \in$ ORD, and let H be a Hilbert space of weight $\aleph_\theta$. There exists a bounded linear operator Φ in H which is a topologically universal morphism in $K^\theta(M)$.

An explicit example of such a linear universal continuous self-map Φ is again easily constructed. Let once more H_o be an arbitrary Hilbert space of weight $\aleph_\theta$, let $H_n = H_o$ for each $n \in N$, and let

(5) $$H = \bigoplus_{n \in N} H_n .$$

If $x = (x_n)_{n \in N} \in H$, we put

(6) $$x\Phi = y = (y_n)_{n \in N} ;$$

with

(7) $$y_n = 2x_{n+1}$$

for every $n \in N$.

4.6. Maps of finite order

In this section some additional remarks are made concerning linearizations of mappings of finite order and of finite semigroups of continuous self-maps. Thus, linearization in finite-dimensional spaces is succinctly discussed; a result of J. DE GROOT on linearization of retractions by orthogonal projections is exhibited, and the latter result is slightly generalized.

Let G be a finite semigroup of continuous self-maps of a metrizable space M; say G has k elements. (As usual, we suppose that $i_M \in G$). Then if H is a Hilbert space into which M can be topologically embedded, the action of G on M can be G-linearized in the Hilbert sum

$$K = \bigoplus_{\gamma \in G} H \tag{1}$$

of k copies of H. A map $\gamma_o \in G$ is linearized by the map $\gamma_o^* : K \to K$ such that

$$(x_\gamma)_{\gamma \in G} \gamma_o^* = (x_{\gamma_o \gamma})_{\gamma \in G} . \tag{2}$$

Suppose now that M is separable and finite-dimensional, say of dimension n. Then, as is well-known, we can take for H the finite-dimensional euclidean space R^{2n+1}. In this case it follows that there exists a G-linearization in $R^{k(2n+1)}$.

In particular, if ϕ is an autohomeomorphism of M of finite order k, then ϕ can be linearized by an orthogonal transformation in $R^{k(2n+1)}$. As a rule, ϕ can even be linearized in an R^m with $m<k(2n+1)$. The least value for m which accommodates all autohomeomorphisms ϕ of fixed finite order k of arbitrary separable metrizable spaces of fixed dimension n has been determined by A.H. COPELAND Jr. and J. DE GROOT [18] in case k is prime, and by J.M. KISTER and L.N. MANN [65] for arbitrary k.

If G is a finite group of autohomeomorphisms of M, the G-linearization in K defined by (2) linearizes the action of G by means of unitary operators in K (by means of orthogonal transformations, if H is an R^n).

If G is a finite semigroup of continuous self-maps of M, this naturally is no longer true. However, in this case the bounded operators γ^* are still of a rather special kind: each of them is a product of a unitary operator and a projection. (We call <u>projection</u> each bounded linear operator P which is idempotent: $P^2=P$. Thus a projection P is not necessarily an orthogonal projection of H onto the closed linear subspace HP).

This is a consequence of the following simple lemma:

4.6.1. LEMMA. Let A be a finite set. If ϕ is an arbitrary map $A \to A$, there exist a 1-1 map ϕ_1 of A onto itself, and idempotent maps $\phi_2 : A \to A$ and $\phi_3 : A \to A$, such that $\phi = \phi_1 \circ \phi_2 = \phi_3 \circ \phi_1$.

PROOF. Let $S \subset A$ such that $\phi|S$ is 1-1 while $S\phi = A\phi$. Then there exists a 1-1 map σ of $A \setminus S$ onto $A \setminus A\phi$, and a 1-1 map $\tau : A\phi \to S$ such that $(\phi \circ \tau)|S = i_S$. We define $\phi_1, \phi_2, \phi_3 \in A^A$ as follows:

(3) $$\phi_1|S = \varphi|S;\ \phi_1|(A \setminus S) = \sigma;$$

(4) $$\phi_2|A\phi = i_A|A\phi;\ \phi_2|(A \setminus A\phi) = \sigma^{-1} \circ \phi;$$

(5) $$\phi_3 = \phi \circ \tau.$$

Then ϕ_1 is 1-1 and onto, $\phi_2^2 = \phi_2$, $\phi_3^2 = \phi_3$, and $\phi = \phi_1 \circ \phi_2 = \phi_3 \circ \phi_1$.

If now G is a finite semigroup, the left translation $\overline{\gamma_o}$ defined by $\gamma_o \in G$ is the composition of a 1-1 map of G onto itself and an idempotent map, by lemma 4.6.1. It follows that the same holds for the bounded operator γ_o^*, defined by (2). Thus we have:

4.6.2. PROPOSITION. Let G be a finite semigroup of continuous self-maps of a metrizable space M of weight $\aleph_\theta$. There exists a G-linearization by a semigroup G^* of bounded linear operators in a Hilbert space K of weight $\aleph_\theta$, such that every $T \in G^*$ is simultaneously of the form $T = UP_1$ and of the form $T = P_2U$, where U is a unitary operator in K while P_1, P_2 are projections.

If $\phi : M \to M$ is a retraction, then $\phi^2 = \phi$, and hence ϕ^* is a projection all by itself. J. DE GROOT, who first observed this, has indicated how this fact can be better set off: it is possible, through a suitable modification of the embedding map $M \to H \oplus H = K$, to linearize ϕ by an orthogonal projection.

4.6.3. PROPOSITION. Let $\theta \in$ ORD, and let H be a Hilbert space of weight $\aleph_\theta$. Let $K = H \oplus H$, and let P be the orthogonal projection of K onto its closed linear subspace $H \oplus \{0\}$. Then P is an "$\aleph_\theta$-universal retraction" : if M is an arbitrary metrizable space of weight at most

$\mathfrak{K}_\theta$, and if ϕ is an arbitrary continuous retraction of M, then ϕ can be linearized by P.

PROOF. Let μ be a topological embedding of M into H; then a topological map $\tau: M \to K$ is defined by putting

(6) $$\xi\tau = (\xi\phi\mu\ ,\xi\mu - \xi\phi\mu)$$

for arbitrary $\xi \in M$. Clearly $\phi\tau = \tau P$.

If more generally ϕ is a continuous self-map of M which generates a finite semigroup, it is once more possible to exhibit more clearly the decomposition of ϕ^* into a unitary operator and a projection; once again it can be obtained that this projection is orthogonal. Suppose the maps $\phi, \phi^2, \ldots, \phi^{n+m-1}$ are pairwise distinct, while $\phi^{n+m} = \phi^n$ ($n \geq 0$, $m \geq 1$). Let μ again be a topological embedding of M into H. We define a map $\tau: M \to H^{n+m}$ as follows: if $\xi \in M$, then

(6) $$\xi\tau = (\xi\phi^n\mu,\ \xi\phi^{n+1}\mu, \ldots, \xi\phi^{n+m-1}\mu\ ,\ \xi\phi^m\mu - \xi\mu\ ,\ \xi\phi^{m+1}\mu - \xi\phi\mu, \ldots, \xi\phi^{n+m-1}\mu - \xi\phi^{n-1}\mu).$$

It is easily verified that τ is a topological map.

Furthermore, we define a unitary operator $U : H^{n+m} \to H^{n+m}$ as follows: if $x = (x_1, x_2, \ldots, x_{n+m}) \in H^{n+m}$, then

(7) $$xU = (x_2, x_3, \ldots, x_m, x_1, x_{m+2}, x_{m+3}, \ldots, x_{m+n}, x_{m+1}).$$

Finally let P be the orthogonal projection of H^{n+m} onto its closed linear subspace spanned by the first n+m-1 coordinates:

(8) $$xP = (x_1, x_2, x_3, \ldots, x_{n+m-1}, 0).$$

Then $\phi\tau = \tau UP$.

Similarly, if Q is the orthogonal projection in H^{n+m} defined by

(9) $$xQ = (x_1, x_2, \ldots, x_m, 0, x_{m+2}, x_{m+3}, \ldots, x_{m+n}),$$

then $\phi\tau = \tau QU$.

As an application of proposition 4.6.3 we present a new proof of the following result of W. NITKA [88] (generalizing a result of

C. KURATOWSKI [69]):

4.6.4. THEOREM. Let M be a metrizable space, A a retract of M, and ρ_A a metric on A corresponding with the relative topology of A induced by M. Then there exists a metric ρ on M, inducing on M the given topology, which satisfies the following conditions:

(i) ρ extends ρ_A; i.e. $(x,y)\rho = (x,y)\rho_A$ whenever $x,y \in A$;

(ii) A is ρ-convex; i.e. if $x,y \in A$ and $z \in M$ such that $(x,z)\rho + (z,y)\rho = (x,y)\rho$, then $z \in A$;

(iii) there exists a map $\phi: M \to A$ such that $(x,A)\rho = (x,x\phi)\rho$, for all $x \in M$.

PROOF. By proposition 4.6.3 we may assume that M is a subset of a Hilbert space K, and that A = (M)P, where P is the orthogonal projection of K onto some closed linear subspace. Then clearly a metric ρ inducing the right topology on M is defined by putting, for arbitrary $x,y \in M$:

$$(x,y)\rho = (xP,yP)_{\rho_A} + \|(x-xP) - (y-yP)\| ; \tag{10}$$

it is immediately verified that ρ satisfies conditions (i)-(iii).

4.7. Linear embedding; universal linear operators

We have seen that infinite direct joins do not exist in K(H) except in trivial cases (corollary 3.2.13). Therefore the standard constructions can not be used in order to obtain universal morphisms; it is likely that $K^\theta(H)$-universal morphisms ($\theta \in$ ORD) do not exist. However, Hilbert sums apparently constitute a reasonably useful substitute for direct joins (cf. the previous sections of this chapter), and by their use some partial results can be obtained. Principal among these results is the theorem of G.-C. ROTA, asserting that in $K^\theta(H)$ there exists a bounded linear operator which is universal for all bounded linear operators with spectral radius less than one.

We recall that the monomorphisms of K(H) are the 1-1 bounded linear operators (proposition 1.2.4). If $\mu: H \to K$ is a monomorphism, then $H\mu$ is a closed linear subspace of K, and $\mu: H \to H\mu$ has a bounded inverse.

4.7.1. DEFINITION. A set S of bounded linear operators in a Hilbert space H is called <u>U-bounded</u> if the semigroup generated by S is bounded in norm. A linear operator $T : H \to H$ is called U-bounded if the set $\{T^n : n \in N\}$ is U-bounded.

In order to abbreviate several formulations below we introduce:

4.7.2. DEFINITION. Let H,K be Hilbert spaces, F a semigroup of bounded linear operators in H, G a semigroup of bounded linear operators in K. We say that <u>G is similar to a restriction of F</u> if there exists a 1-1 bounded linear operator $\mu: K \to H$ and a homomorphism $h : F \to G$ such that

$$\mu \circ \phi = \phi h \circ \mu \tag{1}$$

for all $\phi \in F$.

REMARK 1. Under these conditions it follows that the closed linear subspace $K\mu$ of H is invariant under all $\phi \in F$; if we write μ^{-1} for the inverse of $\mu: K \to K\mu$, then

$$G = \{\mu \circ (\phi | (K\mu)) \circ \mu^{-1} : \phi \in F\} . \tag{2}$$

Let us re-examine the proof of theorem 4.3.1, assuming now that the metric space M considered there is a Hilbert space. If the transformation group G consists of bounded linear operators in M, and if moreover G is U-bounded, say $\|\gamma\| \leq c$ for all $\gamma \in G$, we need not embed M first in a bounded subset of H_o; instead, we will take H_o identical to M. For we can replace 4.3.(3) by the inequality

$$\|(\xi)(\phi h)\| \leq c. \|\xi\|, \tag{3}$$

which warrants that τ maps M into $C(F,H_o)$. As before, τ is 1-1. Moreover, τ is clearly linear; and this makes it much easier to establish the bicontinuity of τ: we need only show that τ is bounded. In fact, as

$$\|\xi\tau\|^2 = \int_F (\phi f)^2 \cdot \|(\xi)(\phi h)\|^2 d\phi \leq c^2 \cdot \|\xi\|^2 \cdot \int_F (\phi f)^2 d\phi, \tag{4}$$

we find that

$$\|\tau\| \leq c \cdot (\int_F (\phi f)^2 d\phi)^{\frac{1}{2}}. \tag{5}$$

In this way we obtain:

4.7.3. PROPOSITION. Let $\theta \in$ ORD, H a Hilbert space of weight $\aleph_\theta$, and F a W-group. There exists a group F^* of bounded linear operators in H with the following property. If K is any Hilbert space of weight at most $\aleph_\theta$, and if G is an U-bounded topological transformation group of bounded linear operators in K which is a continuous homomorphic image of F, then G is similar to a restriction of F^*.

4.7.4. COROLLARY. Let $\theta \in$ ORD, and let H be a Hilbert space of weight $\aleph_\theta$. There exists a (denumerable, free) group F of bounded linear operators in H with the following property. If G is a countable U-bounded group of bounded linear operators in a Hilbert space K of weight at most $\aleph_\theta$, then G is similar to a restriction of F.

Both the hypothesis of U-boundedness and the use of weight functions serve to obtain that the embedding map τ constructed in the proof of theorem 4.3.1 maps M into $C(F,H_o)$. If now G has the property

(6) $$\sum_{\gamma \in G} \|\gamma\|^2 < \infty$$

(which implies that G is countable and U-bounded), clearly no weight is needed: if F is any countable group of which G is a homomorphic image, and if

(7) $$K = \bigoplus_{\phi \in F} M,$$

then G is similar to a restriction of the group F^* of all bounded linear operators ϕ_o^* in K, ϕ_o varying over F, defined by

(8) $$(\xi_\phi)_{\phi \in F}\, \phi_o^* = (\xi_{\phi_o \phi})_{\phi \in F}\,.$$

Clearly these operators ϕ_o^* are unitary; thus we find:

4.7.5. PROPOSITION. Let $\theta \in$ ORD, and let H be a Hilbert space of weight $\aleph_\theta$. There exists a (denumerable and free) group F of unitary operators in H with the following property. If G is a countable group of bounded linear operators in a Hilbert space K of weight $\leq \aleph_\theta$, such that (6) holds, then G is similar to a restriction of F.

And also:

4.7.6. PROPOSITION. Let $\theta \in$ ORD, and let H be a Hilbert space of weight $\aleph_\theta$. There exists a unitary operator U in H with the following property. If T is an invertible bounded linear operator in a Hilbert space K of weight at most $\aleph_\theta$, and if

(9)
$$\sum_{k \in I} \|T^k\|^2 < \infty,$$

then T is similar to a restriction of U.

An example of such an operator U is the bilateral infinite shift; this follows from (8), taking for F the additive group I. Let H_o be a Hilbert space of weight $\aleph_\theta$; let $H_k = H_o$, for each $k \in I$, and put

(10)
$$H = \bigoplus_{k \in I} H_k .$$

Then $U : H \to H$ is defined as follows: if $x = (x_k)_{k \in I}$, then $xU = (x_{k+1})_{k \in I}$. (In the terminology of P.R. HALMOS [52] , the inverse (or adjoint) of U is called the <u>bilateral shift based on H_o</u>, or also the <u>bilateral shift of multiplicity $\aleph_\theta$</u>).

In the same way one can show (cf. the discussion in section 4.4):

4.7.7. PROPOSITION. Let $\theta \in$ ORD, and let H be a Hilbert space of weight $\aleph_\theta$. There exists a (denumerable, free) semigroup F of bounded linear operators in H such that every U-bounded countable semigroup G of bounded linear operators in a Hilbert space K of weight $\leq \aleph_\theta$ is similar to a restriction of F.

4.7.8. PROPOSITION. Let $\theta \in$ ORD, and let H be a Hilbert space of weight $\aleph_\theta$. There exists a bounded linear operator T in H with the following property. If S is any U-bounded linear operator in a Hilbert space K of weight at most $\aleph_\theta$, then S is similar to a restriction of T.

REMARK 2. Let $\varepsilon > 0$. It follows from the fact that $n \to (1+\varepsilon)^{-n}$ is a weight on the additive semigroup N, together with remark 2 of section 4.3, that T can be chosen in such a way that

(11) $$\|T\| \leq 1+\varepsilon .$$

4.7.9. PROPOSITION. Let $\theta \in ORD$, and let H be a Hilbert space of weight $\aleph_\theta$. There exists in H a linear operator U of norm 1 with the following property. If T is a bounded linear operator in a Hilbert space K of weight at most $\aleph_\theta$, and if

(12) $$\sum_{n=1}^{\infty} \|T^n\|^2 < \infty,$$

then T is similar to a restriction of U.

In order to construct explicitly such an operator U, we suppose that H_o is a Hilbert space of weight $\aleph_\theta$, that $H_n = H_o$ for each $n \in N$, and that

(13) $$H = \bigoplus_{n \in N} H_n .$$

Then $U : H \to H$ can be defined as follows:

(14) $$(x_o, x_1, x_2, \ldots)U = (x_1, x_2, x_3, \ldots).$$

(This operator U is the adjoint of the operator U_+,

(15) $$(x_o, x_1, x_2, \ldots)U_+ = (0, x_o, x_1, x_2, \ldots),$$

which is called by P.R. HALMOS [52] the unilateral shift based on H_o, and also the unilateral shift of multiplicity $\aleph_\theta$).

If the spectrum of T lies in the interior of the unit disc, then (12) is valid (see G.-C. ROTA [91] p.470). Hence the following is true:

4.7.10. THEOREM (G.-C. ROTA [91]). Let $\theta \in ORD$, and let H be a Hilbert space of weight $\aleph_\theta$. There exists a bounded linear operator U in H, which is a contraction operator, with the following property. If T is any bounded linear operator in a Hilbert space K of weight at most $\aleph_\theta$ whose spectrum is contained in the interior of the unit disc, then T is similar to a restriction of U to one of its invariant closed linear subspaces.

Applications of this theorem are given in the papers [90,91] of G.-C. ROTA.

4.8. Notes

Since a considerable time several authors have tried to embellish the action of a transformation group G operating on a metric space X through some modifications in X of a non-topological nature. Archetypical is a theorem of S. EILENBERG [35] , from 1936:

4.8.1. THEOREM. If G is a compact group of autohomeomorphisms of a metrizable space M, then M can be metrized in such a way that all transformations $\gamma \in G$ become isometries.

(For an analogous result for locally compact groups, see J. DE GROOT [46]).

For special M and G much stronger results were subsequently obtained. For instance in [109] the following theorem is mentioned:

4.8.2. THEOREM. Let G be a compact transformation group, operating effectively on R^3. Suppose G is not totally disconnected and not finite. Then R^3 can be coordinatized in such a way that G becomes a closed subgroup of the orthogonal group.

A closely related theorem is given in D. MONTGOMERY - L. ZIPPIN [82] :

4.8.3. THEOREM. Let G be a non-trivial connected compact transformation group, operating effectively on R^3. Then the action of G is topologically equivalent either to the group of all rotations around an axis or to the group of all proper orthogonal transformations.

It becomes much easier to recognize the action of G on M as nice if one starts looking at things in a wider perspective; said otherwise, if one allows a topological embedding of M into some bigger space. At first, this bigger space was always taken to be a finite-dimensional euclidean space.

That this really opens up new possibilities can be seen from examples of R.H. BING [14] and of D. MONTGOMERY - L. ZIPPIN [81] (cf. also [82]). R.H. BING constructed a "wild reflection", an involutory homeomorphism of the three-sphere S^3 with a wildly embedded plane as set of fixed points. D. MONTGOMERY and L. ZIPPIN obtained a "wild rotation", a sense-preserving involution of R^3 having a wildly embedded topological line as fixed point set. Such homeomorphisms clearly cannot be linearized in the space itself. They can be linearized, however, in a larger (but still finite-dimensional) space, as we saw in section 4.6. This also follows from results of G.D. MOSTOW (1957):

4.8.4. THEOREM [83] . Let G be a compact Lie group operating faithfully on a separable finite-dimensional metrizable space M. Assume G has only a finite number of "inequivalent orbits" in M. Then G can be linearized by unitary transformations of a euclidean space R^n.

4.8.5. THEOREM [84] . Let G be a compact Lie group of homeomorphisms of a compact manifold M. Then G can be linearized by orthogonal transformations of a euclidean space R^n.

In the case of homeomorphisms of finite order of a finite-dimensional separable metrizable space, the minimal dimension of a euclidean space in which linearization is always possible was determined by A.H. COPELAND Jr. and J. DE GROOT [17] and J.M. KISTER and L.N. MANN [65] ; cf. section 4.6. The last mentioned authors also treat, more generally, the case of compact abelian Lie groups with a finite number of distinct isotropy subgroups, acting on a compact metrizable space.

The next generalization consists in dropping the finite-dimensionality condition on the space in which one linearizes. The study of the possibility of linearization by bounded linear operators in some Hilbert space was originated by J. DE GROOT [48] and A.H. COPELAND Jr. and J. DE GROOT [17,18]. Corollary 4.5.3 is taken from [18] . (It was also asserted by M. KLINE [67] ; however, the proof presented by M. KLINE is incorrect). To J. DE GROOT are also due corollary 4.3.5 (oral communication; cf. also [8]) and corollary 4.3.3 ([49] , Theorem I). A detailed proof of corollary 4.3.3 was presented in the preliminary note J. DE GROOT and P.C. BAAYEN [50] .

Our proof of theorem 4.3.1 is modelled after J. DE GROOT's proof of corollary 4.3.3 in [49] . The new element is the use of weights. A preliminary presentation of this proof is given in [50] .

In this preliminary version [50] , the property of weights expressed by lemma 4.2.2 was incorporated in the definition; we are indebted to G.J. HELMBERG for pointing out to us that this property is a consequence of hypothesis (iii) of definition 4.2.1. The contents of sections 4.2 and 4.3 will also be published elsewhere (P.C. BAAYEN and J. DE GROOT [10]).

Proposition 4.6.3 is due to J. DE GROOT (oral communication), who also suggested the proof presented by us of W. NITKA's theorem 4.6.4; cf. also [6] .

G.-C. ROTA [90] showed that for each fixed transfinite weight (dimension) there exist universal contractions. His proof depended on the same construction which we considered so often, representing points by their orbits; these orbits, in this case, are identified with points of an infinite Hilbert sum. Correspondingly, G.-C. ROTA's universal contraction is an (inverse) unilateral shift. This result was generalized by G.-C. ROTA to bounded linear operators of spectral radius <1 (theorem 4.7.10) in [91] .

The unilateral shift of multiplicity 1 (in the Hilbert sum of a denumberable number of one-dimensional spaces) was thoroughly studied by A. BEURLING [13] . Unilateral shifts of finite multiplicity are considered by P.D. LAX [75] . In P.R. HALMOS [52] both unilateral and bilateral shifts of arbitrary multiplicity are studied and their invariant subspaces are discussed. Shift operators in Hilbert spaces are also studied in connection with the theory of unitary dilations; cf. e.g. I. HALPERIN [55] , also for further references.

REFERENCES

1. P.S. ALEXANDROV, Ueber stetige Abbildungen Kompakter Räume. Proc.Kon.Ned.Akad.v.Wetensch.28 (1926),997-999.

2. P.S. ALEXANDROV, Zur Theorie der topologischen Räume. Dokl.Akad.Nauk S.S.S.R. 11(1936), 55-58.

3. P.S. ALEXANDROV, O ponjatij prostranstva v topologij. Uspekhi Matem. Nauk 2 (1) (1947), 5-57.

4. R.D. ANDERSON, On raising flows and mappings. Bull. Amer. Math. Soc. ...

5. H. ANZAI and S. KAKUTANI, Bohr compactifications of a locally compact group I, II. Proc.Imp.Acad. (Tokyo) 19(1943), 476-480, 533-539.

6. P.C. BAAYEN, Toepassingen van een lineariseringsprincipe. Report ZW 1962-011, Mathematisch Centrum, Amsterdam, 1962.

7. P.C. BAAYEN, Universal morphisms II. Preliminary report WN2, Mathematisch Centrum, Amsterdam, 1963.

8. P.C. BAAYEN, S-maps.Preliminary report WN3, Mathematisch Centrum, Amsterdam, 1963.

9. P.C. BAAYEN and J. DE GROOT, Universal morphisms I. Preliminary report WN1, Mathematisch Centrum, Amsterdam, 1963.

10. P.C. BAAYEN and J. DE GROOT, Linearization of mappings. To appear.

11. H. BACHMANN, Transfinite Zahlen. Berlin - Göttingen - Heidelberg, 1955.

12. S. BANACH, Théorie des opérations linéaires. Warszawa 1932.

13. A. BEURLING, On two problems concerning linear transformations in Hilbert space. Acta Math. 81(1949), 239-255.

14. R.H. BING, A homeomorphism between the 3-sphere and the sum of two solid horned spheres. Annals of Math. 56(1952), 354-362.

15. N.G. DE BRUIJN, Embedding theorems for infinite groups. Proc.Kon.Ned.Akad.v.Wetensch.Ser.A,60 (1957), 560-569.

16. G. CANTOR, Beiträge zur Begründung der transfiniten Mengenlehre I. Math. Annalen 46(1895).

17. A.H. COPELAND Jr. and J. DE GROOT, Linearization of homeomorphisms.
Notices Amer.Math. Soc. 6(1959), 844.

18. A.H. COPELAND Jr. and J. DE GROOT, Linearization of a homeomorphism.
Math. Annalen 144(1961), 80-92.

19. N. CUESTA DUTARI, Teoria desimal de los tipos de orden.
Revista Matem. Hispano-Americana 3(1943), 186-205.

20. D. VAN DANTZIG, Über topologisch homogene Kontinua.
Fund. Math. 14(1930), 102-125.

21. D. VAN DANTZIG, Studien over topologische algebra.
Thesis, Amsterdam, 1931.

22. D. VAN DANTZIG, Zur topologischen Algebra I: Komplettierungstheorie.
Math.Annalen 107(1932), 587-626.

23. D. VAN DANTZIG, Groupes monoboliques et fonctions presque périodiques.
Comptes Rendus 196(1933), 1074-1076.

24. D. VAN DANTZIG, Zur topologischen Algebra II: Abstrakte $\mathcal{L}_\nu$ -adische Ringe.
Compos.Math. 2(1935), 201-233.

25. D. VAN DANTZIG, Zur topologischen Algebra III: Brouwersche und Cantorsche Gruppen.
Compos. Math. 3(1936), 408-426.

26. D. VAN DANTZIG, Neuere Ergebnisse der topologischen Algebra.
Matem. Sbornik (N.S.) 1(1936), 665-675.

27. D. VAN DANTZIG, Nombres universels ou $\nu!$-adiques avec une introduction sur l'algèbre topologique.
Ann.Sci. de l'École Norm.Sup. (3) 53, 275-307.

28. D. VAN DANTZIG und B.L. VAN DER WAERDEN, Über metrisch homogene Räume.
Abh.Math.Sem. Hamburg 6(1928), 367-376.

29. C.H. DOWKER, An imbedding theorem for paracompact metric spaces.
Duke Math. J. 14(1947), 639-645.

30. K. DRBOHLAV, A note on epimorphisms in algebraic categories.
Comm.Math.Univ.Carolinae 4(1963), 81-85.

31. PH. DWINGER, Remarks on the field representations of Boolean algebras.
Proc.Kon.Ned.Akad.v.Wetensch., Series A, 63 (1960), 213-217.

32. PH. DWINGER and F.M. YAQUB, Generalized free products of boolean algebras with an amalgamated subalgebra.

Proc.Kon.Ned.Akad.v.Wetensch., Series A, 66 (1963), 225-231.

33. B. ECKMANN, Über monothetische Gruppen. Commentarii math. Helvet. 16(1943/44), 249-263.

34. A. EHRENFEUCHT and A. MOSTOWSKI, Models of axiomatic theories admitting automorphisms. Fund.Math. 63(1956), 50-68.

35. S. EILENBERG, Sur les groupes compacts d'homéomorphies. Fund.Math. 28(1936), 75-80.

36. S. EILENBERG and S. MACLANE, General theory of natural equivalences. Trans.Amer.Math.Soc. 58(1945), 231-294.

37. A. ESENIN-VOL'PIN, On the relation between local and integral weight in dyadic bicompacta. Dokl.Akad.Nauk S.S.S.R. 68(1949),441-444.

38. A. ESENIN-VOL'PIN, On the existence of a universal bicompactum of arbitrary weight. Dokl.Akad.Nauk S.S.S.R. 68(1949), 649-652.

39. J. FLACHSMEYER, Eine universelle Klasse uniformer Räume. Math.Zeitschrift 80(1962), 12-18.

40. J. FLACHSMEYER, Zu einer topologischer Frage von A.N. KOLMOGOROFF. Archiv der Math. 14(1963), 70-72.

41. R. FRAÏSSÉ, Sur certaines relations qui généralisent l'ordre des nombres rationels. C.R. Acad.Sci.Paris 237(1953), 540-542.

42. R. FRAÏSSÉ, Sur l'extension aux relations de quelques propriétés des ordres. Ann.Sci. de l'École Norm. Sup (3), 71(1954), 363-388.

43. R. FRAÏSSÉ, Quelques notions et problèmes de théorie des relations. Cahiers rhodaniens 12(1963), no. 3.

44. L. GILLMAN, Some remarks on η_α-sets. Fund.Math. 43 (1956), 77-82.

45. W.H. GOTTSCHALK and G.A. HEDLUND, Topological dynamics. Amer.Math.Soc.Coll. Publ. Vol. XXXVI, Providence, R.I. 1955.

45*. J. DE GROOT, Topological classification of all closed countable and continuous classification of all countable pointsets. Proc.Kon.Ned.Akad.v.Wetensch. 48(1945), 237-248.

46. J. DE GROOT, The action of a locally compact group on a metric space.
Nieuw Archief v. Wiskunde (3) 7(1959), 70-74.

47. J. DE GROOT, Universal topological mappings of completely regular spaces.
Preliminary concept, University of Amsterdam, May 1959.

48. J. DE GROOT, Every continuous map is linear.
Notices Amer.Math.Soc. 6(1959), 754.

49. J. DE GROOT, Linearization of mappings. In: General Topology and its Relations to Modern Analysis and Algebra.
Proc. 1961 Prague Symposium, Prague, 1962.

50. J. DE GROOT and P.C. BAAYEN, Linearization in Hilbert space.
Preliminary Report WN4, Mathematisch Centrum, Amsterdam, 1963.

51. J. DE GROOT and R.H. MCDOWELL, Extension of mappings on metric spaces.
Fund.Math. 68(1960), 251-263.

52. P.R. HALMOS, Shifts on Hilbert spaces.
Journ. f.d. reine und angew. Math. 208(1961), 102-112.

53. P.R. HALMOS, A Glimpse into Hilbert space. In: Lectures on Modern Mathematics I, ed. by T.L. SAATY, New York (N.Y.), 1963.

54. P.R. HALMOS and H. SAMELSON, On monothetic groups.
Proc.Nat.Acad.Sci. U.S.A. 28(1942), 254-258.

55. I. HALPERIN, Unitary dilations which are orthogonal bilateral shift operators.
Duke Math. J. 29(1962), 573-580.

56. F. HAUSDORFF, Grundzüge der Mengenlehre.
Leipzig, 1914.

57. A. HELLER, On equivariant maps of spaces with operators.
Ann. of Math. 55 (1952), 223-231.

58. E. HEWITT and K.A. ROSS, Abstract harmonic analysis I.
Berlin, 1963.

59. J.B. JOHNSTON, Universal infinite partially ordered systems.
Proc.Amer.Math.Soc. 7(1956), 507-514.

60. B. JÓNSSON, Universal relational systems (abstract).
Bull.Amer.Math.Soc. 62(1956), 403.

61. B. JÓNSSON, Universal relational systems.
Math.Scand. 4(1956), 193-208.

62. S. KAKUTANI, On cardinal numbers related with a compact abelian group. Proc.Imp.Acad.(Tokyo) 19 (1943), 366-372.

63. I. KAPLANSKY, Infinite Abelian groups. University of Michigan Press, Ann Arbor, 1956.

64. J.L. KELLEY, General topology. New York (N.Y.), 1955.

65. J.M. KISTER and L.N. MANN, Equivariant imbeddings of compact abelian Lie groups of transformations. Math. Annalen 148(1962), 89-93.

66. V.L. KLEE, Convex bodies and periodic homeomorphisms in Hilbert space. Trans.Amer.Math.Soc. 74(1953), 10-43.

67. M. KLINE, Representation of homeomorphisms in Hilbert spaces. Bull.Amer.Math.Soc. 45(1939), 138-140.

68. H.-J. KOWALSKY, Kategorien topologischer Räume. Math. Zeitschrift 77(1961), 249-272.

69. C. KURATOWSKI, Une condition métrique pour la rétraction des ensembles. Comptes Rendus de la Soc. des Sci. de Varsovie 28(1935), 156-158.

70. C. KURATOWSKI, Topology I,II. Monografie Matematyczne, Warszawa, 1952 and 1961.

71. A.G. KUROSH, Prjamye razlozhenija v algebrajcheskikh Kategorijakh. Trudy Moskov. Mat. Obshch. 8(1959), 391-412.

72. A.G. KUROSH, Theory of Groups I,II (2nd edition). New York (N.Y.), 1960.

73. A.G. KUROSH, A.Kh. LIVSHITS and E.G. SHUL'GEIFER, Osnovy teorij kategorij. Uspekhi Mat. Nauk 15, 6(1960), 3-52.

74. A.G. KUROSH, A.Kh. LIVSHITS and E.G. SHUL'GEIFER, Foundations of the theory of categories. Russian Math. Surveys 15(1960), 1-46.

75. P.D. LAX, Translation invariant spaces. Acta Math. 101(1959), 163-178.

76. S. MACLANE, Groups, categories and duality. Proc.Nat.Acad.Sci. U.S.A. 34(1948), 263-267.

77. S. MACLANE, Duality for groups. Bull.Amer.Math.Soc. 56(1950), 485-516.

78. M.A. MAURICE, Over gewicht en dichtheid van topologische ruimten.
Report ZW 1962-010, Mathematisch Centrum, Amsterdam, 1962.

79. M.A. MAURICE, Over gewicht en dichtheid van het product van topologische ruimten; en over het gewicht van de ruimte $\{0,1\}^{\nu}$.
Report ZW 1962-019, Mathematisch Centrum, Amsterdam, 1962.

80. E. MENDELSON, On a class of universal ordered sets.
Proc. Amer.Math.Soc. 9(1958), 712-713.

81. D. MONTGOMERY and L. ZIPPIN, Examples of transformation groups.
Proc.Amer.Math.Soc. 5(1954), 460-465.

82. D. MONTGOMERY and L. ZIPPIN, Topological transformation groups.
New York (N.Y.), 1955.

83. G.D. MOSTOW, Equivariant embeddings in Euclidean spaces.
Ann. of Math. 65 (1957), 432-446.

84. G.D. MOSTOW, On a conjecture of Montgomery.
Ann. of Math. 65(1957), 505-512.

85. A. MOSTOWSKI, Über gewisse universelle Relationen.
Ann. Soc.Polon.Math. 17(1938), 117-118.

86. J.-I. NAGATA, On a necessary and sufficient condition of metrizability.
J. Inst. Polytechn. Osaka City Univ. Ser. A., Math., 1 (1950), 93-100.

87. B.H. NEUMANN and H. NEUMANN, A remark on generalized free products.
J. London Math.Soc. 25(1950), 202-204.

88. W. NITKA, Une généralisation du théorème de Kuratowski sur la caractérisation métrique de la rétraction.
Colloquium mathematicum 8(1961), 35-37.

89. I.I. PAROVIČENKO, A universal bicompact of weight $\aleph$.
Soviet Mathematics (Dokl.Akad.Nauk S.S.S.R.) 4(1963), 592-595.

90. G.-C. ROTA, Note on the invariant subspaces of linear operators.
Rend.Circ.Mat.Palermo Ser. II, 7(1959), 182-184.

91. G.-C. ROTA, On models for linear operators.
Comm.Pure Appl. Math. 13(1960), 469-472.

92. G.-C. ROTA, On the classification of periodic flows.
Proc.Amer.Math.Soc. 13(1962), 659-662.

93. W. RUDIN, Fourier analysis on groups. New York (N.Y.) - London, 1962.

94. W. SIERPINSKI, Sur une propriété des ensembles ordonnés. Fund.Math. 36(1949), 56-67.

95. W. SIERPINSKI, Cardinal and ordinal numbers. Monografie Matematyczne, Warszawa, 1958.

96. Yu.M. SMIRNOV, On metrization of topological spaces. Uspekhi Mat.Nauk 6(1951), 100-111.

97. Yu.M. SMIRNOV, Ob universal'nykh prostranstvakh dlja nekotorikh klassov beskonetsnomernnykh prostranstv. Izv. Akad.Nauk S.S.S.R. Ser.Mat. 23 (1959), 185-196.

98. J. SONNER, On the formal definition of categories. Math. Zeitschrift 80(1962/63), 163-176.

99. A.H. STONE, Paracompactness and product spaces. Bull.Amer.Math.Soc. 54(1948), 977-982.

100. A. TYCHONOV, Über einen Metrisationssatz von P. URYSOHN. Math. Annalen 95 (1925), 139-142.

101. A. TYCHONOV, Über die topologische Erweiterung von Räumen. Math. Annalen 102(1929), 544-561.

102. A. TYCHONOV, Über einen Funktionenraum. Math. Annalen 111 (1935), 762-766.

103. A. TYCHONOV, Über einen topologischen Universalraum. C.R. Acad.Sci. U.R.S.S. 3(1936), 49-51.

104. P. URYSON, Zum Metrisationsproblem. Math. Annalen 94(1925).

105. P. URYSON, Mémoire sur les multiplicités Cantoriennes. Fund.Math. 7 (1925), 30-137.

106. P. URYSON, Sur un espace métrique universel I,II. Bull.Sc.Math. (2) 51 (1927), 43-64 and 74-90.

107. N.B. VEDENISOV, Remarque sur la dimension des espaces topologiques. Moskov.Gos.Univ.Uch.Zap. 30(1939), 131-146.

108. A. WEIL, L'intégration dans les groupes topologiques et ses applications. Paris, 1940.

109. L. ZIPPIN, Transformation groups. In: Lectures in topology, ed. by R.L. Wilder and W.L. Ayres. Ann. Arbor (Mich.), 1941.

110. W. SIERPINSKI, Sur les espaces métriques universels. Atti Accad. Sci. Torino 75 (1940), 571-574.

111. W. SIERPINSKI, Sur un espace métrique séparable universel. Atti Accad. Sci. Torino 75 (1940), 575-577.

112. W. SIERPINSKI, Sur un espace métrique séparable universel. Fund. Math. 33 (1945), 115-122.

113. W. SIERPINSKI, Sur les espaces métriques universels. Fund. Math. 33 (1945), 123-136.

114. W. SIERPINSKI, General Topology (transl. C.C. Krieger). Toronto, 1952.

APPENDIX: LIST OF CATEGORIES

I. The following categories were introduced in section 1.2:

K(S) - category of all mappings of one set into another.

K(LO) - category of all order-preserving maps of one linearly ordered set into another one.

K(PO) - category of all order-preserving maps of one partially ordered set into another.

K(La) - category of all lattice-homomorphisms of one lattice into another lattice.

K(DLa) - the full subcategory of K(La) obtained by admitting as objects only distributive lattices.

K(BA) - category of all boolean homomorphisms of one boolean algebra into another one.

K(SGU) - category of all homomorphisms of one semigroup with unit S_1 into another semigroup with unit S_2, which send the unit of S_1 into the unit of S_2.

K(G) - the full subcategory of K(SGU) obtained by admitting only groups as objects.

K(AG) - the full subcategory of K(SGU) obtained by admitting only abelian groups as objects.

K(M) - category of all continuous maps of one metrizable space into another one.

K(ZM) - category of all continuous maps of one zero-dimensional metrizable space into another.

K(CZ) - category of all continuous maps of one compact zero-dimensional space into another such a space.

K(CR) - category of all continuous maps of one completely regular Hausdorff space into another.

K(H) - category of all bounded linear operators of one Hilbert space into another.

K(CMAG) - category of all continuous homomorphisms of a compact metrizable abelian group into another compact metrizable abelian group.

K(CMoG) - category of all continuous homomorphisms of one compact monothetic group into another.

II. In the remainder of the text the following categories are mentioned (the numbers of the sections in which they occur are added between brackets):

K(C) - category of all continuous maps of one compact Hausdorff space into another (1.6; 3.4).

K(ZH) - category of all continuous maps of one zero-dimensional Hausdorff space into another (1.6).

$K(T_o)$ - category of all continuous maps of one T_o-space into another T_o-space (1.6).

K(CS) - category of all continuous homomorphisms of one compact solenoidal group into another (1.4; 2.5; 3.1).

K(ZCMoG) - category of all continuous homomorphisms between zero-dimensional compact monothetic groups (1.4; 2.5; 3.1).

III. If K is a concrete category and if $\theta \in$ ORD, then $K(\theta)$ denotes the full subcategory of K obtained by restricting the class of objects of K to all those which have a cardinal number $\leqq \aleph_\theta$. Instead of $K(S)(\theta)$ we write $K(S,\theta)$, etc.

If K is a category of topological spaces and if $\theta \in$ ORD, then K^θ denotes the full subcategory of K obtained by restricting the class of objects of K to all those with weight at most $\aleph_\theta$.

IV. In addition to the categories listed in I and II, and their subcategories obtained as indicated under III, a few other categories were mentioned or described. For these categories, however, no special symbols were introduced. For this reason we will not list them here.

РЕЗЮМЕ

По известной теореме А.Тихонова всякий куб (топологическое произведение отрезков) P_κ веса κ (κ – некоторое трансфинитное кардинальное число) является универсальным вполне регулярным пространством веса $\leq \kappa$. Следуя более недавным результатам, оказывается существование даже универсальной системы F_κ непрерывных отображений P_κ в себя: если X вполне регулярное пространство веса по крайней мере κ , и если S какаянибудь полугруппа содержащая по крайней мере κ непрерывных отображений X в себя, то действие полугруппы S топологически эквивалентно действию F суженному на подходящее инвариантное при F подпространство куба P_κ (см. [47,49]).

Основная идея доказательств этого результата поразительно проста. В краткости она изложена в заметках главы 2. Здесь мы замечаем только что она по существу ограничается рассмотрением орбитов точек X , определенных пологруппой S , как элементов нового пространства.

Эта основная идея показывается очень ценной тоже в других обстоятельствах. Й. де Хроут (J. DE GROOT) и автор пользовались ее при решении (положительном) проблемы Андерсона о существовании универсального гомеоморфизма дисконтинуума Кантора(см. [6]).Точно тем же способом доказал Г. Ц. Рота (G.-C. ROTA) [90,91] существование универсальных контракцыенных операторов пространства Гильберта. Эти факты привели к систематическому рассмотрению основной конструкции в общем виде; для того показался очень удобным язык теории категорий.

Скажем что морфизм $\alpha : A \to A$ категории K эквивалентен сужению морфизма $\beta : B \to B$ в K, если существует мономорфизм $\mu : A \to B$ так что $\mu B = \alpha\mu$. Морфизм $\beta : B \to B$ в K называется универсальным в K, если всякий (эндо-)морфизм $\alpha : A \to A$ эквивалентен сужению β. В работе показывается, что основную конструкцию можно перевести на язык абстрактных категорий и получить общие достаточные условия существования универсальных морфизмов.

В главе 1, еще до развивания этой теории, мы дадим перечень некоторых идей и результатов из литературы, которыми мы будем пользоваться дальше, по требованию пополняя их. В абзацах 1.1 и 1.2 мы вводим основные понятия теории категорий, перечень некоторых конкретных категорий (которыми мы будем пользоваться в применениях общих результатов и тоже такие, которые будут служить материалом для некоторых контрпримеров), в котором по возможности определены мономорфизмы и эпиморфизмы в соответствующих категориях.

Если $\beta : B \to B$ - универсальный морфизм категории K, то B является универсальным объектом в следующем смысле: для всякого объекта A категории K существует мономорфизм $\mu : A \to B$. Значит, раньше чем искать универсальные морфизмы необходимо спрашивать о существовании универсальнного объекта. К щастью, много результатов о универсальных объектах можно найти в литературе; некоторые из них сосредотогены в абзаце 1.4. В абзаце 1.3 мы приняли терминологию Б. Йонсона (B. JÓNSSON) [60,61] , так как его теорема о универсальных системах отношений является одним из самых важных и ценных результатов в этом направлении.

В абзаце 1.5 рассматривается структура монотонных отображений линейно упорядоченных множеств по мере необходимости для доказательства (в следующей главе) существования универсальных морфизмов в категориях линейно упорядоченных пространств. Эти категории исключительны (к этому факту мы вернемся); кроме абзаца 2.7 результатами абзаца 1.5 мы никде не пользуемся.

Заключение главы 1, и вообще заключение всякой главы, посвещено заметкам и добавлениям к материалу главы. В частности, здесь рассмотрена подробнее литература касающаяся этой главы.

В главе 2 рассматривается основная конструкция на языке теории категорий. Определяются универсальные морфизмы, универсальные биморфизмы и универсальные системы морфизмов. Дополнительно, вводятся дуальные понятия (абзац 2.1).

Следующие два абзаца посвящены частным случаям морфизмов: эти морфизмы аналогичны тем преобразованиям произведения X^A, которые только определены переменой координат точек $(x_\alpha)_{\alpha \in A} \in X^A$. Результатами этих абзацев мы пользуемся в абзаце 2.4, чтобы получить простое достаточное условие, которое обеспечивает существование универсального морфизма в K.

Теорема 1. Если K содержит универсальный объект u и если в K существует прямая сумма счетного числа экземпляров u, то K содержит универсальный морфизм.

(Мы обобщаем этот результат для универсальных систем морфизмов; рассмотрим тоже случай морфизмов универсальных только для подкатегории K_o категории K. Сформулированы тоже дуальные результаты.)

Существует много применений теорем существования сформулированных в абзаце 2.4. Некоторые из них показаны в абзаце 2.5. Для примера мы отмечаем:

Теорема 2. Пусть κ трансфинитное кардинальное число. Существует автоморфизм (эндоморфизм) $\phi : A \to A$ группы (абелевой группы, булевой алгебры, дистрибутивной структуры) A, который универсален для всех автоморфизмов (эндоморфизмов) $\phi : B \to B$ любой группы (абелевой группы, булевой алгебры, дистрибутивной структуры) B такой, что $\mathrm{card}(B) \leq \kappa$. Если имеет место обобщенный континуум гипотез, и если еще $\kappa^{\aleph_0} = \kappa$, то получаем даже что $\mathrm{card}(A) = \kappa$.

Теорема 3. Существует непрерывный автоморфизм (эндоморфизм) ϕ бесконечномерного тора, который универсален для всех непрерывных автоморфизмов (эндоморфизмов) любых компактных абелевых групп.

Получаются подобные результаты о существовании универсальных непрерывных отображений в себя, или автогомеоморфизиов метризуемых пространств, или компактных нульдимерсиональных отделимых пространств ограниченного веса, и о универсальных монотоных отображениях частично упорядоченных пространств. Все эти результаты обобщены для универсальных систем морфизмов.

Следующие два теоремы являются примерами применений дуального характера:

Теорема 4. Пусть κ трансфинитное кардинальное число. Существует автоморфизм (эндоморфизм)некоторой группы (абелевой группы, полугруппы с единицей, булевой алгебры, дистрибутивной структуры) A - мы обозначаем его $\Phi : A \to A$ -, $\mathrm{card}(A) = \kappa$, обладающий следующим свойством: если B группа (абелева группа, полугруппа с единицей, булевая алгебра, дистрибутивная структура), $\mathrm{card}(B) \leq \kappa$, и если $\varphi : B \to B$ - автоморфизм (эндоморфизм) B, то φ может выть накрыто отображением Φ.

Теорема 5. Существует непрерывный автоморфизм (эндоморфизм) Φ компактной соленоидальной группы G, который накрывает всякий автоморфизм (эндоморфизм) любой компактной соленоидальной группы H - накрытие и морфизмы разумеются непрерывными.

Более того, показаны примеры категорий обладающих универсальным объектом но несодержащих универсальный морфизм. Тоже показано, что достаточное условие теоремы 1 нет условием достаточным: в абзаце 2.7 мы доказываем, что в категории всех монотонных отображений линейно упорядоченных множеств (кроме некоторых тривиальных случаев) не существуют прямые суммы, все таки здесь существуют монотонные отображения в себя, универсальные для всех отображений в себя линейно упорядоченных множеств мощности меньше или ровно κ (κ - любое трансфинитное кардинальное число).

В третьей главе мы рассматриваем категории топологических пространств. Результаты главы 2 можно усилить в следующем смысле: в определениях и утверждениях можно заменить понятия мономорфизма и эпиморфизма понятиями гомеоморфизма в и непрерывного отображения на соответственно. Абзац 3.4 содержит несколько применений. К ним относятся новые доказательства некоторых результатав о S -компактификации работы Й. де Хроута (J. DE GROOT) и Р. Г. МэкДоуэла (R.H. MCDOWELL) и результата Р. Д. Андерсона (R.D. ANDERSON), касающегося накрываний непрерывных отображений в себя преобразованием множества Кантора. (См. [51, 4].) Рассматриваются тоже равномерно непрерывные отображения в равномерных пространствах и универсальные изометрии и контракции в метрических пространствах. В абзаце 3.5 мы обращаем внимание на теорему о универсальном непрерывном отображении вполне регулярного пространства (замеченной уже в начале резюме) и особенно ее интерпретации как результата о линеарисации отображений.

Основным результатом главы 4 (теорема 4.3.1) является обобщение теоремы Й. де Хроута (J. DE GROOT) [49] , утверждающая что действие компактной группы автогомеоморфизмов метризуемого пространства эквивалентно действию группы G унитарных операторов пространства Гильберта, суженному на подходящее G -инвариантное подмножество H .Показывается , что локально компактную группу преобразований G , действующую на метризуемом пространстве M можно линеаризировать при помощи группы линейных операций в некотором пространстве Гильберта, как только G принадлежит классу CW . Класс CW , определенный в абзаце 4.2, содержит не только все компактные группы, но тоже счетные дискретные группы, аддитивную группу действительных чисел. Более того, всякая подгруппа и всякий непрерывный гомоморфный образ группы из CW принадлежит классу CW ; прямое топологическое произведение конечного числа групп из класса CW тоже в классе CW , всякая локально компакгная группа G , содержащая такую компактную нормальную подгруппу G_o что G/G_o дискретная и счетная, содержится в классе CW . Следовательно, CW содержит все локально компактные абелевы группы, которые или сепарабельные или компактно порожденные; в конечно, в этом классе содержатся даже и некоторые неабелевы группы.

В абзаце 4.4 рассматриваются возможности (по видимому ограниченные) расширения этих результатов для полугрупп топологических преобразований. Показывается каким образом из доказательства теоремы 4.3.1 вытекают некоторые результаты о универсальной линеарисации. Абзац 4.6 дополнительные информации для частного случая отображений конечного порядка и для конечных полугрупп преобразований.

(Результаты этих первых шести абзацев главы 4 будут тоже напечатаны отдельно: П.Ц. Байэн и Й. де Хроут (P.C. BAAYEN, J. DE GROOT) [10].)

Абзац 4.7 посвящен универсальным ограниченным линейным операторам определенного вида в пространстве Гильберта. Г. Ц. Рота (G.-C. ROTA) [90,91] доказал что одностороний (обратный) сдвиг универсален для всех операторов T с радиусом спектра меньше единицы. Мы показываем, что существует ограниченный линейный оператор, который универсален для всех T таких , что все итерации T^n равномерно ограниченны по норме. Подобные результаты получаются для равномерно ограниченных полугрупп линейных операторов.

Printed at the Mathematical Centre at Amsterdam,49,2nd Boerhaavestraat.
The Netherlands.

The Mathematical Centre, founded the 11th of February 1946, is a non-profit institution aiming at the promotion of pure mathematics and its applications, and is sponsored by the Netherlands Government through the Netherlands Organization for Pure Scientific Research (Z.W.O.) and the Central National Council for Applied Scientific Research in the Netherlands (T.N.O.), by the Municipality of Amsterdam and by several industries.